The NASA Technology Transfer Program

Samuel I. Doctors

The Praeger Special Studies program—utilizing the most modern and efficient book production techniques and a selective worldwide distribution network—makes available to the academic, government, and business communities significant, timely research in U.S. and international economic, social, and political development.

The NASA Technology Transfer Program

An Evaluation of the Dissemination System

PRAEGER SPECIAL STUDIES IN U.S. ECONOMIC AND SOCIAL DEVELOPMENT

Praeger Publishers　　New York　Washington　London

PRAEGER PUBLISHERS
111 Fourth Avenue, New York, N.Y. 10003, U.S.A.
5, Cromwell Place, London S.W.7, England

Published in the United States of America in 1971
by Praeger Publishers, Inc.

© 1971 by Praeger Publishers, Inc.

Library of Congress Catalog Card Number: 79-158103

Printed in the United States of America

To Harvey Brooks

ACKNOWLEDGMENTS

I owe a debt of gratitude for assistance in this research project to several score of people in private industry, at NASA, at various Regional Dissemination Centers, at several research centers, at Harvard, and at MIT. I am particularly indebted to my thesis committee, Dean Harvey Brooks and professors Paul Cherington and Richard Rosenbloom. Their help and detailed comments on several drafts assisted me in the course of this research. In addition, professors Donald Marquis and Edward Roberts of MIT provided valuable advice and commented on various sections of the project.

I am also indebted to the industrial clients of the New England Research Application Center who gave so generously of their time during my field-work interviews. A number of clients of the Aerospace Research Applications Center assisted the project by completing my questionnaires.

Len Rawicz and Gayle Parker of the NASA Headquarters legal staff have been most helpful in providing data on various aspects of government patent/license policy.

Robert Jolkovski and Peter Glaser of Arthur D. Little, Inc. were most generous with their time and offered me insight into their studies of the transfer process.

Dean Coddington and his colleagues at the Denver Research Institute provided data on their transfer studies and commented on my research outline. Their help was particularly important for Chapter 2, which draws on the results of a number of their transfer studies for NASA.

The Science and Public Policy Program of the Harvard School of Public Administration contributed greatly to the creation of this book through its library and through the opportunities it provided for discussion with eminent scientists and administrators.

A number of very kind and patient women have assisted me in the preparation of this manuscript; among them Nancy Matthews, Lenore Abraham, and Mary McConahay must be cited for their especially valuable assistance.

Finally, David Banner, a doctoral candidate at Northwestern University Graduate School of Management, provided most valuable assistance in preparing the final draft manuscript for publication.

CONTENTS

LIST OF TABLES

LIST OF FIGURES

LIST OF ABBREVIATIONS

ADL	Arthur D. Little, Inc. (consulting firm)
AE	Applications Engineer (NERAC)
AEC	Atomic Energy Commission
AIAA	Aerospace Industries Association of America
ARAC	Aerospace Research Application Center (RDC at University of Indiana)
CA	Current Awareness (search)
CFSTI	Clearinghouse for Federal Scientific and Technical Information (Department of Commerce)
CQ	Client Questionnaire
DDC	Defense Documentation Center (DOD)
DOA	Department of Agriculture
DOD	Department of Defense
DRI	Denver Research Institute
ERC	Electronics Research Center, Boston, Mass. (NASA Research Center)
FCST	Federal Council for Science and Technology
GPO	Government Printing Office (Washington, D.C.)
IAA	International Aeronautics Abstracts (issued by AIAA)
IITRI	Illinois Institute of Technology Research Institute

IR&D	Independent Research and Development (overhead costs on government contracts)
KASC	Knowledge Availability Systems Center (RDC at University of Pittsburgh)
MRI	Midwest Research Institute (Kansas City, Mo.)
NASA	National Aeronautics and Space Administration
NERAC	New England Research Application Center (RDC at University of Connecticut)
NPA	National Planning Association
NSF	National Science Foundation
OTU	Office of Technology Utilization (NASA)
R&D	Research and Development
RDC	Regional Dissemination Center
RS	Retrospective Search
SCTQ	Selected Corporate Technologist Questionnaire
SIC	Standard Industrial Classification (a numerical code for classifying industries)
STAR	Scientific and Technical Aerospace Reports
STID	Scientific and Technical Information Division (NASA)
STS	State Technical Services (Department of Commerce program)
TU	Technology Utilization (NASA)
TUD	Technology Utilization Division (NASA)
TUO	Technology Utilization Officer (NASA)
TUP	Technology Utilization Program (NASA)

The NASA Technology Transfer Program

1

TECHNOLOGY TRANSFER IN THE
FEDERAL AGENCY SETTING

Concern with the process of technology transfer[1] from federally sponsored research and development (R&D) programs to other sectors of the economy began with the rapid increase in federal R&D spending which was initiated in the early 1950's by such external stimuli as the need for rapid creation of an intercontinental ballistic missile weapon system, and was accelerated even more rapidly after the Russian Sputnik in 1957. There was a sharp increase in federal R&D expenditures between 1956 and 1964, when they rose from $3.4 to $14.7 billion, or from 5.2 percent of direct federal budget expenditures to 12.4 percent. Since fiscal 1964 federal R&D expenditures have grown to over $17 billion in fiscal 1970, excluding overhead R&D funding and capital expenditures.[2]

Although the level of federal R&D spending has now stabilized, and has actually declined as a percentage of total R&D spending since fiscal 1965, there is still much concern with the secondary application of the products of federally sponsored R&D. Federal R&D programs accounted for about 8.7

percent of direct federal budget expenditures in
fiscal 1970 (from a high of 12.6 percent in 1965)
but, more important, these federal R&D expenditures
accounted for about 60-65 percent of all R&D spending in the United States during the fifteen-year
period 1955-70.[3]

Since economic growth is thought to be highly
correlated with R&D spending,[4] this trend to concen-
tration of much of the U.S. R&D spending in federal
government programs (and on a limited number of
space/defense programs) rather than in private industry has been seen by some as a possible inhibitor
of overall economic growth.[5] The evidence for this
inhibition is inconclusive, however, since the overall effect of this increased market for R&D may have
created a larger pool of trained technical manpower
and, more important for this study, may have made a
greater choice of new technology available for commercial industrial use, given efficient transfer
mechanisms. Further, federal R&D programs are often
initiated in areas where commercial enterprises fear
to tread, such as high-risk, long-term payoff projects, whereas most commercial R&D programs are not
very high risks and have a time horizon of three to
five years or less.[6] Thus, federal R&D may stimulate more rapid development of many new areas of
technology, such as atomic power and composite materials.

The focus of this study is those present policies and programs of the federal government which
tend to encourage and/or inhibit transfer of technology from the vast federal R&D program. This
analysis includes the reaction of commercial industry to these policies and programs and, in particular, industry's use of federal transfer programs.
Almost everyone agrees that encouraging a faster
rate of transfer would generally benefit the economy, but areas of lesser agreement are the following:

1. How much transfer has already occurred and
by what means?

2. Can transfer of technology from federal R&D be encouraged by a deliberate program?

3. What pace of transfer can or should be encouraged?

4. What should be the distribution of responsibility between public and private sectors for encouraging transfer?[7]

5. Is a national policy for transfer needed?

A basic difficulty in answering any of these questions is the lack of substantive data regarding the transfer process in the federal agency context. Most of the studies of the diffusion process thus far have focused on the diffusion of technology from innovation to users within the same industrial or institutional setting.[8] This type of transfer has been labeled vertical transfer. On the other hand, very little research has been done with respect to the quite different problems involved in transferring technology created in one institutional setting to a quite different institutional setting, such as from space/defense R&D programs to commercial industry (commonly called horizontal transfer).[9]

This study will not attempt to provide comprehensive answers to the five questions; rather, it will seek to provide additional substantive data regarding the effectiveness of present federal programs and policies in enhancing technology transfer, and their impact on industry. Recommendations will also be made for policy changes in present federal agency programs and for additional transfer studies which might lead to more effective federal agency transfer programs.

THE NASA TRANSFER PROGRAM

This study will focus primarily on the National Aeronautics and Space Administration (NASA) transfer program, the most fully articulated transfer program within a federal science agency.

The NASA program has been the largest and most
elaborate transfer program aside from the Department
of Agriculture's (DOA) Cooperative Extension Service, and until recently it was the only sizable federal program aimed at horizontal transfer. The
State Technical Services (STS) program was established in late 1965 within the Department of Commerce to promote horizontal transfer, and its federal and state matching funds appear to have ex-
ceeded NASA transfer expenditures in 1968. The STS
program estimates total federal and state expenditures of over $12 million for fiscal 1968.[10] It
went out of existence in 1969 as a result of Congress' failure to extend its initial three-year
life.

NASA transfer expenditures are quite difficult
to compute since the Technology Utilization Program
(TUP) figures do not include employee salaries,
laboratory and field office expenditures, that portion of NASA Scientific and Technical Information
Division (STID) activities which should be appor-
tioned to TUP activities, or contractor reimburse-
ment for costs of reporting new technology.

The NASA program has an extensive acquisition
subsystem for the collection of aerospace technology
from its own contractors, from NASA laboratories,
from other government agencies, and from a variety
of foreign sources. An evaluation subsystem uses a
series of technology utilization officers (TUO) at
each NASA laboratory, a field office to monitor reporting of new technology by NASA employees and contractors, and a number of contractors to provide
more detailed evaluation of this new technology for
"commercial potential."[11]

The NASA program has adopted a variety of dissemination and transfer techniques, including NASA-
sponsored conferences and seminars, establishment
of regional libraries, sponsorship of three biomedical application groups, cooperative programs
with other federal agencies, and consultation with
visitors to NASA laboratories and field offices.[12]

However, the largest and most novel part of the dissemination program has been the establishment of a
series of university-based regional dissemination
centers (RDC) in most regions of the United States.
These RDC's are considered by NASA to be modeled after the DOA's Cooperative Extension Service college-
based experiment and dissemination centers. One
major difference in structure is that the NASA RDC's
themselves make the bulk of the user contact, whereas in the DOA program the functionally separate
county agents make most of the detailed user contact. Another major difference is the symbiotic relationship between government programs (federal and
state), farm-support industry, and the farmer that
has greatly facilitated transfer of many new areas
of technology in agriculture.

Coupled with these extensive NASA acquisition,
evaluation, and dissemination subsystems is a very
elaborate set of patent/license regulations. These
regulations are designed, in part, to promote the
other portions of the transfer program by encouraging reporting by contractors and use of NASA-
developed technology through selective grants of
title for commercial application of patentable items
to the contractors, and through selective granting
of licenses (non-exclusive and exclusive) to third
parties.[13]

This very extensive NASA transfer program has
provided an opportunity to study, in depth, all
parts of an ongoing federal agency horizontal transfer system and its interaction with industrial users.
It has been possible to observe the influence of a
variety of policy decisions on the effectiveness of
transfer, such as the decision to concentrate RDC
efforts on immediate commercial industrial transfer
and the decision to place the TUO's administrative-
ly under the direction of the laboratory or field
office (and not under the administrator for technology utilization [TU]).. It is not suggested that
exact causal links can be established between NASA
policy decisions and the effectiveness of the transfer program, but extensive observation and analysis

of the system indicate that a number of general effects on the program resulting from a variety of
policy decisions can be identified.

The NASA program was established largely in response to political pressures to show some tangible
payoff for all the promises of spin-off and spillover made early in the space program. The need to
establish a transfer program quickly led to a program which was based largely on expediency, not on
research results concerning the transfer process.
Furthermore, to date there has not been much systematic research sponsored to provide data for more effective policy formulation.* Rather, the program
has been used largely as a vehicle to gather statistics of document distribution to industry for Congressional hearings. This has led to avoidance of
controversial transfer experiments, such as those
taking an entrepreneurial approach to transfer. It
has been assumed that collecting large numbers of
technical reports in the aerospace area, storing
them in a semi-automated retrieval system which included a smaller number of specific innovation reports, and making these reports available through
the university-based RDC's would result in significant and measurable transfer.[14]

Much can be learned for future transfer programs from a detailed study of the NASA program and
a detailed analysis of industrial reaction to this
program. Also, insight can be gained about the horizontal transfer process in general by examining industrial use or non-use of NASA-supplied space/
defense technology.

---

*Some studies generally in the area of horizon-
tal transfer have been sponsored by NASA, such as
those by Donald Marquis and Edward Roberts and their
colleagues at MIT and some smaller ones at Arthur D.
Little, Inc., but they were discontinued when the
results were shown to differ from TU expectations.

OUTLINE OF THE STUDY

This study forms the second part of a larger
research effort. Part I, which was published in
mid-1969, was a study of the present federal role
in technology transfer, including a detailed study
of the acquisition portion of the NASA TUP.[15] It
provided some of the background for the field study
portion of this study. It must be emphasized that
while the present study has a direct relationship
to the earlier, more general study, it represents a
distinct contribution by itself.

This study reports an investigation into the
effectiveness of the present TU system of regional,
university-based dissemination centers. The purpose
has been to determine the relative effectiveness of
the present NASA system, which emphasizes dissemination of technical documents to fee-paying industrial
clients, and to compare this RDC system with other
transfer mechanisms. The present study contains the
following:

1. A discussion of the purposes of this RDC
field study, together with an analysis of the relevant transfer framework. Within this framework, the
hypotheses of the study are presented and discussed.

2. The results of both the field study and the
comparison study are analyzed, together with the results of a number of recent, more general studies of
the horizontal transfer process. The purpose of
this analysis is to determine the overall effectiveness of the NASA transfer program as compared with
other transfer mechanisms, including (1) new
technology-based company spin-offs, (2) technologist
mobility, (3) patent grant to contractors alone, and
(4) licensing of government patents to third parties.

3. The results of the field study are compared
with the results of other studies of RDC effectiveness, and with other more general studies of the
NASA transfer program, to determine the relative
value of the RDC as a transfer mechanism.

4. A general survey of the institutional framework of RDC transfer, including overviews of federal science agency transfer policies, an analysis of the NASA dissemination program, and a detailed discussion of RDC operations and policies is provided.

5. An analysis of the results of a field study of NASA RDC industrial clients is made to determine what types of transfer have occurred and under what circumstances.

6. Finally, an overall set of conclusions is drawn on the basis of both parts of the study, and a set of recommendations for future federal transfer programs and policies is formulated. These conclusions include the following: (1) the present NASA program has not generated technology transfer equal to its cost, either in terms of specific item transfer or in terms of more general area transfer; (2) the program has not done what it might even to analyze its negative results in order to increase our understanding of the horizontal transfer process; and (3) programs must be instituted by the government to deepen our understanding of the transfer process and thus allow us to better utilize our public investment in R&D.

NOTES

1. Technology transfer is defined as the process whereby technical information originating in one institutional setting is adapted for use in another institutional setting. See Samuel I. Doctors, The Role of the Federal Agencies in Technology Transfer (Cambridge, Mass.: The MIT Press, 1969), pp. 3-6, for an analysis of this concept.

2. See Doctors, op. cit., pp. 10-19, for a detailed analysis of federal R&D patterns and policies over the last three decades. See also NSF, Federal Funds for Research, Development, and Other Scientific Activities: Fiscal Years 1968, 1969, and 1970, NSF 69-31 (Washington, D.C.: U.S. GPO, August, 1969), pp. 2-5.

3. See Doctors, op. cit., Ch. 2, notes 3, 4;
NSF, Research and Development in Industry, 1967,
NSF 69-28 (Washington, D.C.: U.S. GPO, July, 1969),
pp. 5-9; and NSF 69-31, pp. 2-5.

4. Edwin Mansfield, The Economics of Technological Change (New York: W. W. Norton, 1968), pp.
10-41.

5. See Robert Solo, "Gearing Military R&D to
Economic Growth," Harvard Business Review, XL, 6
(November-December, 1962), 49-60; and U.S. Congress,
House of Representatives, Select Committee on Gov-
ernment Research (the Elliott Committee), Hearings
(Washington, D.C.: U.S. GPO, 1964) for discussion
of this problem.

6. See Mansfield, op. cit., pp. 65-68; Richard
Nelson, Merton Peck, and Edward Kalachek, Technology,
Economic Growth, and Public Policy (Washington, D.C.:
The Brookings Institution, 1967), pp. 53-56; and
Jack Carlson, "Aspects of the Diffusion of Technology
in the United States," paper presented to the 5th
Meeting of Senior Economic Advisors, Economic Commis-
sion of Europe, United Nations (Geneva, October 2,
1967), p. 18, for discussions of the expected pay-
back period for industrial R&D.

7. See Richard Rosenbloom, Technology Trans-
fer--Process and Policy, Special Report No. 62
(Washington, D.C.: NPA, 1965), pp. 29-31, for a
discussion of the issue of responsibility between
public and private sectors.

8. See, for example, Everett Rodgers, Diffusion of Innovation (New York: The Free Press, 1962);
James Coleman, Elihu Katz, and Herbert Menzel, Medical Innovation: A Diffusion Study (New York: Bobbs-
Merrill, 1966); Elihu Katz, Martin Levin, and Herbert Hamilton, "Traditions of Research on the Diffusion of Innovation," American Sociological Review,
XXVIII (April, 1963), 237-52; or Bryce Ryan and Neal
Gross, "The Diffusion of Hybrid Corn in Two Iowa
Communities," Rural Sociology, VIII, 1 (March, 1943),
15-24.

9.   See Harvey Brooks, The Government of
Science (Cambridge, Mass.: The MIT Press, 1968),
Ch. 10, pp. 255-59, for a discussion of the distinc-
tions between vertical and horizontal transfer; see
also Doctors, op. cit., Ch. 1, pp. 1-2.

10.   U.S. Department of Commerce, Office of
STS, Annual Report, Fiscal Year 1968 (Washington,
D.C.: U.S. GPO, 1968), p. 41. Also see Doctors,
op. cit., Ch. 5, note 5, for a discussion of some
of the difficulties in establishing accurate estimates of science agency expenditures for transfer--
fiscal 1968 NASA expenditures are between $5 and $10
million. See U.S. Congress, House of Representatives, Committee on Science and Astronautics, Subcommittee on Advanced Research and Technology, 1970
NASA Authorization, Hearings, 91st Congress, final
session (Washington, D.C.: U.S. GPO, 1969), pp.
707-23.

11.   See Doctors, op. cit., Ch. 7, for a detailed discussion of the NASA acquisition and evaluation subsystems. Direct commercial application
has always been the major criterion for reporting
of new technology by contractors and for selection
for inclusion in special NASA publications, such as
Tech Briefs and Special Surveys.

12.   See this study, Table 2, for a detailed
listing of all present NASA dissemination techniques.

13.   See Doctors, op. cit., Ch. 10, for a detailed discussion of NASA patent/license policy effects on transfer.

14.   See Doctors, op. cit., Ch. 6, for a further elaboration.

15.   See Doctors, op. cit.

2

**A COMPARISON
OF HORIZONTAL
TRANSFER
STUDIES**

A number of studies have investigated the process of horizontal transfer. Some have focused on
the NASA transfer program, and a few have specifically investigated the effectiveness of the NASA
RDC's. Another group of studies has investigated
other mechanisms for the transfer of aerospace technology for commercial market application. This
chapter will discuss the findings of these studies
and will compare them with the findings of the fieldwork portion of this study.

STUDIES OF THE NASA TRANSFER PROGRAM

Surveys of RDC Effectiveness

Three surveys of RDC clients investigated the
effectiveness of the RDC program. The earliest of
these was made by the House Subcommittee on Advanced
Research and Technology (Committee on Science and
Astronautics) in mid-1965 and was reported in 1966
during the NASA authorization hearings. Most of
the work for this study was done by Richard Carpenter of the Library of Congress' Legislative Reference Service (Science Policy Research Division),
under the direction of Congressman John W. Wydler

of New York. Mr. Carpenter, during an interview in
the fall of 1968, said that the report in the hearings represented all of his relevant findings. Carpenter has generally given the NASA TUP high marks
for its effectiveness as a transfer mechanism, although the survey results indicate that the program
had not been very effective.[1] The purpose of the
survey was to determine the "return" on the national
investment of $15.464 million in the NASA TUP
through fiscal 1966.[2]

A complete list of RDC client companies as of
June 30, 1965 (eighty-nine companies in all), was
obtained from the NASA TUP. All of these companies
were clients of the Aerospace Research Application
Center (ARAC). Each was contacted by a letter which
stated that the House Science and Astronautics Committee was conducting an inquiry to determine their
"frank and candid opinions as to the operation of
this program [NASA RDC program] from the point of
view of return on your investment and what improve-
ments could be made in the way the program is being
conducted."[3]

Table 1 is a partial listing of the results of
the survey. These results were "not encouraging."
Seventy-one companies replied (81 percent), but
only ten of these were enthusiastic. Five of the
ten were small companies which had used some of the
materials in their work.* Of the fifty-one companies that thought the program was worthwhile,
forty-one offered reservations. All hoped the program would improve its relevance with time.[4] The
study assumed that the seventeen companies that did

---

*Research during the first part of this study
(1966-67) uncovered the fact that over 75 percent
of all ARAC clients were included in Fortune's list
of the 500 largest U.S. corporations. This figure
changed to about 55 percent by 1969 because of a
change in ARAC pricing structure, apparently under
some pressure from NASA to obtain more smaller clients

not reply "could be counted as negative as fear of
offending appears the only logical reason for failure to respond."[5]

TABLE 1

Congressional ARAC Client Survey Results

Number of Replies	Percent of Sample	Comment
51	72.0	Program is worthwhile
7	9.9	Program not worthwhile or too expensive
10	14.0	Tangible benefits
20	28.0	Material often not applicable
18	25.4	Will renew
5	7.0	Will not renew
48	68.0	No comment

Source: U.S. Congress, House of Representatives, Committee on Science and Astronautics, Subcommittee on Advanced Research and Technology, 1967
NASA Authorization. Hearings, 89th Congress, second
session (Washington, D.C.: U.S. GPO, 1966), pp.
642-55.

ARAC/NERAC Studies

Both the Aerospace Research Application Center
(RDC at the University of Indiana) and the New
England Research Application Center (NERAC, RDC at
the University of Connecticut) conducted surveys of
their impact on client companies (both were conducted

during late 1967 and early 1968). The ARAC survey
was divided into two parts:[6] the first was a specially funded survey of general external technical
information usage by twenty-five of their clients;
the second was an informal survey of client transfers
fers resulting from ARAC supplied information. The
NERAC survey was an informal survey of client company transfers.[7] Neither of the surveys clearly defined what was meant by transfer,* nor did they dis-
tinguish between client usage of space/defense-
supplied information and non-space/defense information. Items included in the surveys ranged from
specific item transfers of space/defense technology
to open literature usage for building a library or
providing background for technical problem solving.**

The first part of the ARAC survey consisted of
a series of fifty-six interviews with client personnel, in twenty-five companies, concerning their
usage of externally supplied technical information.
The interviewers made use of a formal questionnaire
as a guide for the interviews.

The major results of the first part of the survey indicated the following:[8]

1. Externally generated information was used
primarily for general background, while internal
sources were used for specific problem solving and
new product ideas.

---

*Specific item transfer has been defined as the
transfer of a specific item of technology such that
it is incorporated in the work product of some individual, can be identified, and can have a dollar
value placed on its contribution, some end item of
this work product.

**These surveys provide the only data other than
the present study of the impact of these two RDC's
on their industrial clients.

2. Twenty-five examples of "new technology obtained externally" were identified by the fifty-six interviewees. Seven or eight of these resulted from ARAC services.[9] These seven or eight instances of technology obtained externally include such items as training program evaluation materials, background material on growing ruby lasers, and obtaining reprints of professional society meetings. Thus the main focus of this portion of the ARAC study was not on transfer, but on information dissemination activities.

3. Literature was identified most frequently as the source of externally generated technology, with consultants second and professional societies third.[10] This finding agrees with that of a Denver Research Institute (DRI) study of channels of external technology used by commercial firms.

The results of the informal five-year transfer survey were the following:*

1. Ten examples of anonymous transfer were identified. Most appeared to be of general background information. No monetary value was placed on these by recipients.[11]

2. Fifteen additional examples of transfer are described. Some appear to be specific item transfers and some are more general background area transfers. Recipients were willing to place a total value of about $25,000 on four of the transfers; values

----

*It is not clear from this report what time period is covered by the survey, but since it accompanies the five-year final report, I have assumed that it covers the same period. The report does indicate that the transfers presented in the report are not to be construed as the only examples identified. But, given the value the NASA TUP places on every fragment of aerospace transfer, it seems unlikely that an RDC contractor would omit many.

were considered too speculative or indeterminate for the other eleven.[12]

The NERAC informal survey of client transfers turned up nine examples of specific item transfer or potential transfer, but only four of the nine would be considered specific item transfers by the definition in this study,* and two or three of these four are examples of open literature, non-space/defense technology transfer. The other five consist of supplying specialized, non-space/defense materials to a library-builder; providing background information for a space/defense agency proposal; one general background transfer for the purpose of bringing a company vice-president up to the state-of-the-art; supplying general background data to a consulting firm; and the sale of a search to another division of the same company because of the first division's satisfaction with NERAC services.

The findings of these three studies generally agree with those of the present fieldwork, in that:

1. Most of the companies surveyed in the Congressional study indicated that they thought the program was worthwhile, but only 14 percent felt that RDC-supplied technology had a value equal to or greater than its cost.

2. Little specific item transfer was found to result from the RDC's dissemination programs.

3. The ARAC survey indicated that RDC-supplied information was used by their clients primarily for general background information, not for new product ideas.

4. The NERAC survey uncovered only a few transfers.

---

*Two of these four were identified in the course of the fieldwork. Both are only potential transfers, since neither has yet been applied.

5. Both RDC surveys indicated that the primary
"transfer" activity was the selective dissemination
of technical literature and that no regular system
of feedback was used, nor were any experimental programs or transfer studies being conducted, because
of NASA budgetary constraints.

More General Studies

A study performed for the NASA TUP by the DRI
sought to establish what channels of technical information were employed by commercial industry, with
particular emphasis on external sources of technical
information, especially space/defense sources.* The
sample was composed of sixty-two industrial firms
from four manufacturing industries--batteries, printing and reproduction machinery, industrial controls,
and medical electronics--and from eleven vocational/
technical education institutions. The data were obtained through the use of 480 self-administered
questionnaires from two sources: two-thirds from
individuals within the seventy-three organizations
visited and the remaining one-third from published
mailing lists. The respondents were classified into
three general groups: research-oriented, product-
oriented, and technical management.

The methodology of this report is not entirely
satisfactory. DRI reports that only 21 percent of
all respondents considered government technology
irrelevant to their work. The problem is the phras-
ing of the question: "Is government technology

----

*This DRI study was not directed so much at
the process of technology transfer as at one element of the transfer process, that of technical information communication. See DRI, op. cit. It is
included among the comparison studies because some
of its findings provide some generally favorable
evidence to substantiate the hypotheses. It is
also indicative of the type of study commonly funded
by the TUP: a mainly passive study of technical
information dissemination, not an experimental study
of transfer.

pertinent to my job?" To answer this negatively may
be to show oneself unprogressive and generally apa-
thetic to sophisticated new technology. No cross
check appears to have been built in to guard against
a natural inclination not to put oneself in a bad
light. Thus, this 21 percent figure is probably
quite low. The fact that the majority of respondents had not even heard of most common government
sources of information, such as the Clearinghouse
for Federal Scientific and Technical Information
(CFSTI), and that less than one-third had used any
of these common sources indicates that this 21 percent figure is not a true indicator of industrial
perception of the relevance of government developed
technology.

The major findings of relevance for this comparison are the following (see also Table 2):

1. Respondents indicated that internal channels of technical information were nearly equal in
importance to all external channels and this was
particularly true for the two non-research oriented
groups.[13]

2. Generally there was heavy reliance on textbooks and handbooks for problem solving, while trade
publications and scientific journals were used primarily for current awareness.

3. The ratio of those using any of these government sources was higher in the more technically
sophisticated industries, such as batteries and
medical electronics, and this usage of government
sources was highly correlated with the respondent's
experience in space/defense R&D and research orientation.[14]

4. Government information sources rated low
for problem solving, and many respondents had not
heard of government sources, particularly NASA
sources of technical information. Less than half
of those respondents who had heard of the government sources of information made any use of these

sources: CFSTI, Scientific and Technical Aerospace
Reports (STAR), Defense Documentation Center (DDC),
International Aeronautics Abstracts (IAA), NASA
Tech Briefs, and NASA Special Reports.[15]

   5. Very few respondents (16 percent) had
heard of the NASA RDC's, and fewer still (4 percent)
made any use of their technical information.*

TABLE 2

Use of Specific NASA and Other Government
Sources of Technical Information
(as percent of total sample)

Source	Heard About	Have Used	Will Continue to Use
NASA Tech Briefs	56	32	25
NASA RDC's	18	5	4
CFSTI	40	28	24
IAA	17	6	5
STAR	24	14	12

   Source: DRI, The Channels of Technology Acquisition in Commercial Firms and the NASA Dissemination Program, NASA-sponsored report (Springfield,
Va.: CFSTI, June, 1967), p. 47.

_____

   *The continued usage rates for those already
using RDC's is consistent with the ARAC questionnaire results but is far different from the NERAC
renewal rate of less than 25 percent. Of course,
the DRI study was constructed during 1966-67, and
probably includes mainly ARAC client firms.

Hayes Study of Electronic Firms'
Transfer Interests

A recent study of transfer investigated the effectiveness of federal programs in assisting a selected group of electronics firms to transfer space/defense technology for commercial application.[16] The study used mail questionnaires as a sampling device, and the sample was composed of seventy electronics firms that returned questionnaires. A breakdown of the sample is provided in Table 3. All but one or two of the companies sold substantial amounts of their output in the space/defense market. Sixty-eight percent of the firms expressed an interest in increasing their percentage of commercial business, and over 84 percent had attempted to transfer the results of their space/defense technology.[17] Most of the firms felt that only a small number of their commercial product ideas came from government-sponsored work. (See Table 4.)

TABLE 3

Sample Composition of Hayes Study

Type of Company	Number of Question-naires	Number Returned	Percent of Sample
NASA Electronics Research Center contractors	38	30	79
Top NASA contractors (selected from 100 largest)	25	15	60
Greater Boston electronics firms ("random sample")	30	25	83
Total	93	70	75 (avg.)

Source: Richard Hayes, "A Study of the Transfer of Technology from Government Sponsored R&D to Commercial Operations in Selected Electronics Companies," unpublished doctoral dissertation (Washington, D.C.: American University, 1968), p. 29.

TABLE 4

Company-Perceived Sources of Commercial
Product Ideas, Hayes Study

Number of Firms	Percent of Sample	Source of Ideas
42	60	Company-sponsored R&D
11	15.7	Commercial customers
7	10	Government-sponsored technology
10	14.3	None

Source: Richard Hayes, "A Study of the Transfer of Technology from Government Sponsored R&D to
Commercial Operations in Selected Electronics Companies," unpublished doctoral dissertation (Washington, D.C.: American University, 1968), p. 214.

Given the fact that most of these firms are
substantial government contractors, it is probable
that a large portion of what is called "company-
sponsored R&D" is composed primarily of space/
defense overhead R&D funding.[18] Unfortunately, the
study provides no breakdown by sources of funds,
nor does the study indicate the amount of successful transfer.

Another finding of the study was that 70 percent of the firms knew of the NASA RDC's, but only
27 percent made any use of their services. And few
of the firms felt that any federal transfer programs were presently of great importance to their
internal transfer programs. They also felt that
technical publications were of little value for
transfer. Direct interpersonal communication was
identified as the principal transfer mechanism.[19]
Most firms indicated that patents on government-
sponsored inventions played little part in commercial

application, with less than 5 percent of all dis-
closures to agency sponsors resulting in new commercial products.[20]

Thus, these results indicate that technically
sophisticated electronics companies are quite interested in horizontal transfer and most have tried to
effectuate transfer within the last few years. However, the study does not indicate whether the smaller firms were more successful than the larger contractors or vice versa, nor does it indicate the
relative amount of transfer of either type of firm.
The study does indicate that about one-fourth of
the sample made use of RDC's for technical literature, but such literature was not viewed as an important stimulus for new commercial products.[21]

The Hayes study focused on the firm as the
unit of analysis; the next study to be considered
examined the use of externally generated invention
reports as the unit of analysis.

DRI Study

A relatively large-scale, long-term project to
study the utilization of NASA Tech Briefs was
started at DRI in late 1967. This project was
funded at $250,000 per year and was a follow-up to
Tech Brief studies conducted at the University of
Maryland between 1964 and 1967.

These Maryland studies were conducted in two
major phases. The first, during 1964 and 1965, attempted to interest companies in NASA Tech Briefs
by a broad mail campaign. Fifteen hundred companies
were contacted, but very little tangible transfer
could be uncovered.[22]

The major focus of the DRI study was on following up requests for Technical Support Packages (TSP)
of Tech Briefs. TSP's are collections of background
material provided for most Tech Briefs and are supplied by NASA laboratories or field offices to anyone requesting additional data concerning a Tech

Brief.[23] Tech Briefs are one- or two-page summaries of a given NASA-developed invention, analytical technique, or other discrete bit of technical data thought by NASA to have "commercial" value. Each Tech Brief contains the name and address of the NASA laboratory or field office where it originated and directs interested readers to contact that facility for additional data. TSP's are usually supplied in answer to such requests. They were the result of a number of complaints by users that Tech Briefs contained insufficient data to make any real judgment about their value.

The Arthur D. Little, Inc., experimental project to sell NASA inventions to industry complained that insufficient data were available with the Tech Briefs they were trying to sell to industry, and they had to supplement the briefs in order to get anyone in industry even to consider application.[24]

The DRI Project for the Analysis of Technology Transfer sent a one-page questionnaire to each individual requesting a TSP. An IBM card file including 18,000 requests was established; 11,000 were statistically analyzed; about 5,600 of the 11,000 requestors returned questionnaires to DRI and about 300 telephone and personal follow-ups were made, representing those cases where transfer or potential transfer was identified or where the information proved of "great value" to the respondent's work. Of the 2,092 Tech Briefs published prior to April, 1968, eighty-nine accounted for over 70 percent of all TSP requests.

A check of the DRI data file indicated that sixteen NERAC clients--three Connecticut firms and thirteen Massachusetts firms--had requested TSP's. Only two of these fell within the potential transfer class, and both were turned up in the fieldwork.*

---

*DRI allowed me to examine their files on Connecticut and Massachusetts firms requesting TSP's in February, 1969. These two cases of potential transfer had been identified in my fieldwork, and the DRI data further confirmed my findings.

No other examples of transfer or potential transfer
involving Tech Briefs used by NERAC clients was
turned up by either study. No other NERAC clients
indicated more than limited usage of Tech Brief
materials.

As may be seen from Table 5, 8.6 percent of
the respondents indicated that they either considered NASA Tech Briefs as providing "information of
great value" (8.1 percent) or as resulting in a new
commercial product or process (0.5 percent).* Although the sample composition is somewhat different
from that used in the fieldwork, the 8.6 percent
figure compares quite well with the figure of 10.5
percent horizontal transfer or potential transfer
found in the fieldwork.** Of course, the DRI category of "provided information of great value to my
work" may not be quite the same as the potential
transfer category in the fieldwork interviews.
Still, the results of the DRI Tech Brief study do
indicate that only a small amount of specific item
transfer has resulted from this portion of the NASA
dissemination program and that this method of literature dissemination is apparently no more effective
as a transfer mechanism than the RDC's.

---

*These percentages of positive usage may be
even lower if one assumes that some substantial proportion of the 4,400 non-respondents were deterred
from providing negative responses. See also the
DRI quarterly evaluation reports dated July 15 and
October 18, 1968, for a description of the 300 telephone and personal follow-ups of TSP's and for detailed methodology discussion.

**For comparison purposes with the NASA Tech
Brief transfer rate, I have eliminated the one example of transfer of open literature, non-space/
defense chemical data to a commercial chemical company and the potential application of the MIT stress
programs by a paper machinery manufacturer. (See
Ch. 6, section entitled "Transfer and Potential
Transfer of Specific Items.")

TABLE 5

Information Evaluation by All Respondents
to DRI Study

Evaluation	TSP Requests	
	Number	Percent
Of no value	183	3.3
Increased my knowledge of state-of-the-art	2,373	42.1
Not applicable to my work	273	4.8
Provided information of limited value to my work	1,793	31.9
Provided information of great value to my work	454	8.1
Resulted in a commercial product or new process	26	0.5
Other	238	4.2
Unknown	289	5.1
Total	5,629	100.0

Source: DRI, Project for the Analysis of Technology Transfer, report to NASA, OTU, Contract NSR 06-004-063 (Denver: DRI, November, 1968), p. 22.

About 50 percent of both the DRI and fieldwork samples stated that the space/defense literature supplied was of some value, primarily as general technical background, not for new product ideas.

Companies falling in the machine tool industrial group made comparatively little use of NASA Tech Briefs, despite the fact that almost one-third

of the briefs are directed at such areas as machine
tool design or machine shop practices. This result
agrees with the generally negative attitude of the
eight machinery and machine tool companies in the
NERAC sample.[25] Companies in technically sophisticated industrial groups, such as electrical machinery, chemicals, and scientific instruments, form
almost 50 percent of the total Tech Brief users if
we exclude government, individual, and educational
service requests. (See Table 6.) These technically sophisticated industrial groups would still account for over 33 percent even if all categories of
requestors were included. This generally high receptivity to space/defense technology found among
technically sophisticated industrial groups agrees
quite well with the findings of the fieldwork as
measured both by RDC usage and renewals for RDC
information.

TABLE 6

Distribution of All TSP Requests by Predominant
Standard Industrial Classification

SIC Code	Industry	TSP Requests Number	Percent
36	Electrical machinery	2,264	20.6
82	Educational services	1,035	9.4
35	Non-electric machinery	857	7.8
28	Chemicals	821	7.5
91	Federal government	785	7.1
00	Individuals	712	6.5
38	Scientific instruments	590	5.4
37	Transportation equipment	556	5.0
89	Miscellaneous services	339	3.1
	All others	3,054	27.6
Total		11,013	100.0

Source: DRI, Project for the Analysis of Technology Transfer, report to NASA, OTU, Contract NSR
06-004-063 (Denver: DRI, November, 1968), p. 12.

MORE GENERAL STUDIES OF THE
HORIZONTAL TRANSFER PROCESS

There have been a number of studies directed
generally at the broad problem of horizontal transfer of space/defense technology.[26] Some of these
studies, such as the DRI study of commercial application of missile/space technology and the Watson
and Holman study of the commercial application of
NASA-sponsored inventions, have concentrated on
measuring quantitatively the amount of transfer
that has occurred, while others, such as the Roberts
study of MIT spin-off firms and the Shimshoni study
of technical entrepreneurship in the scientific instrument industry, have been more concerned with the
methodology of transfer. This chapter will examine
both types of study: the first generally to test
the findings of the fieldwork; and the second to examine the effectiveness of alternative methods of
transfer. Several of the studies, such as the
patent/license studies, deal with both the identifiable transfer issue and the alternative methods
of transfer issue. The transfer studies to be discussed in this chapter are not exhaustive of those
performed in recent years, but they do represent
the bulk of the scholarly work done in the area
through the end of 1969.

Although there had been a number of opinion
surveys about the value of space/defense R&D for
the American economy, little serious study of the
problem had been done prior to the publication in
1963 of the DRI study of horizontal transfer of
aerospace technology.[27] The primary purpose of
that study was to find and document examples of
transfer from aerospace technology to commercial
industry. The initial effort was to find specific
item transfers; but as the study progressed, it became quite clear that the horizontal transfer process did not readily admit such easily identifiable,
discrete by-products or spin-offs. Rather, the
study concluded that "The total contribution of
missile/space R&D to the commercial economy is

broader, more complex, more indirect, and more difficult to identify than is generally realized . . .
contrubution . . . [of] by-products are but a fraction of the whole."[28]

The study found that what had been transferred
was most often general areas of knowledge, not specific aerospace by-products. The DRI study also
found that transfer occurs more easily within a
single organizational entity, be it a division of a
large corporation or a smaller company, rather than
across organizational lines. The study also found
that claims for or against various horizontal transfer methods designed to promote a faster rate of
transfer were based on intuition or guesses, not
substantive knowledge about inter-firm transfer.[29]
It is interesting to note that one of the conclusions was that present efforts to facilitate transfer are handicapped by insufficient knowledge of
transfer at the level of the firm. Shortly after
the publication of this report, NASA Administrator
James Webb authorized the TUP to fund the Marquis-
Roberts studies. Their studies and that of Shimshoni represent the most comprehensive studies of
transfer at the level of the firm. The NASA TUP
has not acted or shaped its policies on the basis
of the results of the MIT or Harvard studies.

Marquis-Roberts Spin-off Studies

The studies of Marquis and Roberts and their
colleagues at the MIT Sloan School are of great importance for our knowledge of the transfer process,
since they represent the most comprehensive studies
of intra-firm technology diffusion. Of particular
importance for comparison purposes are several findings of Roberts' Boston Route 128 spin-off company
studies.[30]

Roberts' sample represented 115 companies spun
off from the MIT laboratories, fifty-one from MIT
academic departments, sixteen from the Air Force
Cambridge Research Laboratory, five from MITRE, and
thirty-nine from a single, large electronic systems

contractor. The companies were an average of five
years old at the time of the study. Some variation
was found among these five groups in their rates
and degrees of transfer and in other measured para-
meters, but the figures given for comparison purposes represent composite figures cited by Roberts.
The MIT spin-offs were, for instance, markedly more
successful in transfer than were the spin-offs from
the large electronics systems contractor.

The internal entrepreneur or champion is crucial for the transfer of very sophisticated space/
defense technology, and the small, technically
based firm provides an organization very conducive
to the success of his transfer activities. The 226
spin-off firms which form Roberts' sample started
almost exclusively as government contractors and/or
subcontractors. Within five years they averaged,
as a group, 40 percent transfer to the commercial
market, and the rate of transfer was increasing.[31]
The role of the government in the transfer process
was primarily to provide an initial market for the
expensive, technically sophisticated products and
to provide some overhead funding to cover development costs.[32]

Shimshoni Study

A study that built on the work of Marquis and
Roberts was that of Daniel Shimshoni. He performed
an extensive study of the scientific instrument industry in order to determine the nature of innovation in this industry and to study the innovators
who have created this dynamic science-based industry since the end of World War II.[33] He was specifically interested in discovering the factors
that affect the founding and growth of these new
technical firms. His sample consisted of 141 scientific instrument firms, located mainly in California
and in the Northeast. His principal findings of importance here are the following:

1. Technical entrepreneurship and spin-off
firms greatly accelerate the rate of innovation.

2. Technologist mobility is a key element in transfer.

3. Government-sponsored technology has been the primary basis of innovation in the scientific instrument industry.

Arthur D. Little Study

The three previous studies examined existing phenomena; in contrast, Arthur D. Little, Inc. (ADL) performed an experimental field study of commercial/ industrial acceptance of a set of twenty carefully selected NASA inventions described in Tech Briefs. These twenty inventions were presented to twenty-three companies during seven months of 1965.[34] Both the inventions and the company's new technology needs were carefully matched prior to any contact. Also, market needs for each invention were determined. Contact was through personal on-site meetings with company personnel interested in the given areas of new product development. During 1965, three inventions were sold to four companies and had reached the stage of company-funded development or production. The ADL project was not renewed by NASA, and thus contact with the other nineteen companies was not maintained.

ADL did work for NASA in the transfer area since the inception of the TUP till their contract was discontinued in 1967; it consisted mainly of reviewing NASA contractor or employee flash sheets to determine their "commercial" relevance and then writing Tech Briefs from the "commercially" relevant flash sheets. This small, experimental program was merely an add-on to the larger ADL Tech Brief writing project; it was dropped soon after it showed its first results, because the NASA Office of Technology Utilization (OTU) felt that it was not within its charter to sponsor such a market-oriented approach to transfer. The argument advanced was "How can NASA sponsor a project which assists one industrial firm and not its competitor?"

It should be noted that the three inventions marketed during these early efforts were low-cost, low-risk inventions and that ADL provided marketing consultation and obtained additional development data for the four companies. The inventions were an improved silicate paint, an RF feedthrough (radio frequency circuit), and an improvement in gas bearings.[35]

The conclusions of this brief experimental project were the following:[36]

1. A skilled new product consultant could obtain access to an "attentive audience" for NASA inventions in most companies.

2. It was often difficult to obtain additional development data for interested companies, particularly where the inventor was a contractor, not a NASA employee.

3. Specific item transfer of space/defense inventions is probable only where an entrepreneurial approach is adopted by the external transfer agent and a market need which fits the invention he is attempting to transfer has first been identified by this external transfer agent.

4. A longer-term and more difficult problem was thought to be that of obtaining feedback on NASA invention applications once a company had decided to undertake further development, since the safest course for a company was to divulge as little new product development information as possible.

The Roberts and Shimshoni studies both concentrated on studying the effects of technical entrepreneurship and technologist mobility on horizontal transfer, while the ADL project concentrated on trying to use an entrepreneurial approach to transfer space/defense technology. Another group of researchers has examined a quite different stimulus for transfer, that provided by the patent system.

Agency Patent Policy Studies

The patent system in the more usual commercial
context is thought to encourage innovation through
the mechanism of providing monopoly profits to the
inventor (or his successors in interest) for a
seventeen-year period. In the government sector,
patents have also been thought to provide a spur to
commercial application of government-sponsored R&D
by-products. Two primary mechanisms have been used
by the government to encourage commercial application: in many situations federal agencies will
grant the patent title to the industry inventor for
commercial application of a government-sponsored
invention; and in other instances, where the government has title to an invention, licenses may be
granted to third parties. Usually the licenses are
non-exclusive, though exclusive licenses have been
granted on a few occasions.[37]

Great interest in the utilization of government-
sponsored and/or -owned patents began with the establishment of NASA A series of studies of agency
patent policies was initiated under the direction
of the Patent, Copyright and Trademark Subcommittee
of the Senate Judiciary Committee.[38] This subcommittee and others in both houses of Congress have
held numerous hearings on government agency patent
policy since 1958, particularly on the policies of
the major science agencies.[39] Great concern has
been raised at the specter of government-sponsored
R&D by-products being given away to large space/
defense contractors.[40] Others have raised equally
violent objection to withholding the patent grant
from contractors whose technology the government is
using to develop our space/defense programs and
then withholding title to inventions based largely
on these contractors' private funds.[41]

The results of Project Hindsight and an examination of federal R&D spending patterns pretty
clearly indicate that space/defense technology today
is largely the result of government-sponsored R&D,
not private R&D investment.[42] But, whatever the

moral or ethical allocation of patent rights between
the government and its space/defense contractors,
we are here concerned primarily with the effectiveness of the patent or license device as a spur to
transfer.

Harbridge House/Watson and Holman Studies

The most thorough and comprehensive studies of
both government contractor and third party usage
were conducted by two George Washington University
economists, Donald Watson and Mary Holman,[43] and by
a team of researchers at Harbridge House, Inc.[44]
The former study covered only NASA contractors and
third party licensees of NASA patents. The latter
report covered most other federal agency contractors
and licensees.

Before discussing the results of these studies,
it shouls be noted that patents and licenses play a
far different role in the government market than
they do in the commercial sector of the economy.
Even if a patent is developed entirely with private
funds, it may often afford the patent holder or his
licensees little protection in bidding for government work, because of the interpretation given to
provisions of the Patent Cases Act of 1948.[45] The
interpretation of this act by a series of court and
administrative agency decisions generally requires
a federal agency, when evaluating competing bids of
a patentee or his licensee and a possible infringer
of the patent, to consider only the lower price,
not potential patent infringement costs. The stat-
ute provides as a sole remedy for the aggrieved
parties a suit against the United States in the
Court of Claims.

On the other hand, when the patent is developed
under federal agency R&D funds, the contractor or
third party licensee can obtain only a right to apply the invention for commercial application. The
government always retains a royalty-free license
for any governmental application. Once an invention is reported for the purpose of filing a patent,

it becomes part of the public domain insofar as governmental application is concerned. Thus, government contractors may lose their competitive edge in
the government market by patenting a novel idea.

Whether for this reason or because government
R&D is simply not performed in areas likely to pro-
duce patentable inventions, government contractors
have over the years filed patents at about 10 percent of the rate common for commercial R&D.[46]
Thus, patents do not play as large a role in the
government sector as they do in the commercial market. Utilization of government-sponsored patents
ranges from 7 to 15 percent, while commercial utilization has been estimated at 60 percent.[47] Still,
these patents are one transfer mechanism that can
be more easily measured than many others, and
therefore, we will examine the results of the
Watson and Holman and Harbridge House studies.

Watson and Holman surveyed all organizations
and persons who had been granted title to a NASA-
sponsored invention through 1965. They also surveyed all NASA licensees. They employed only mail
questionnaires as their data collection device.[48]
The study concluded that NASA contractors were
largely indifferent to NASA patent policy, few applied for easily obtainable individual or blanket
waivers and of those who did apply for waivers,
even fewer had commercially exploited them.[49] Less
than 1 percent of NASA contractor-owned inventions
had been successfully applied.[50]

Forty-seven NASA-owned patents had been li-
censed and of these forty-seven, five had received
some commercial use. Another fifteen were said to
have some commercial potential.[51] Thus, industrial
usage of NASA inventions appeared to be quite low.

The Harbridge House study attempted to measure
more generally the impact of federal agency patent
policies on the commercial application of both
contractor-owned patents and third party licensees.
Their sample was all government-sponsored inventions

patented in the two years 1957 and 1962. This two-
year sample included 2,024 contractor-owned inventions and 126 government-owned inventions.[52] The
study methodology consisted of mail questionnaires
sent to all contractors holding title to one or more
patents granted in 1957 and/or 1962, and to all licensees of the 126 government-owned patents (342
licensees). Sixty percent of the questionnaires
were returned. They were analyzed and used to select certain patentees or licensees for detailed
case analyses, usually those firms which had commercially exploited an invention.* The three agencies accounting for more than 90 percent of the R&D
funding--DOD, NASA, and the Atomic Energy Commission (AEC)--also accounted for more than 98 percent
of the patents arising under government contracts
during the two sample years.[53]

The results of the study indicated the following:

1. Total commercial sales of the exploited inventions amounted to $616 million through 1966, $406
million by contractors and $210 million by govern-
ment licensees, compared with agency R&D expenditures of $4.9 billion in fiscal 1957 and $10.2 billion in fiscal 1962.[54] All but $271,000 of the
contractor patent sales were attributed to DOD-
sponsored inventions.

2. Sales were concentrated in just a few inventions: 88 percent of the contractor sales were
concentrated in five inventions, and about half of
the licensee sales were concentrated in three patents for the manufacture of potato flakes.[55]

---

*Five groups of case studies were conducted:
(1) twenty-one high and low utilizers of sample inventions; (2) all sampled TVA and DOA inventions;
(3) usage by sixteen education and non-profit organizations; (4) all sampled inventions involved in
infringement suits; and (5) effects of NIH policy on
industry participation in government R&D.

3.   Companies either predominantly in the government market or in the commercial market made
little use of government patents. Firms doing 20
to 80 percent government business used these patents
much more often.[56]

4.   The main reason given for non-utilization
was "limited" direct commercial applicability.[57]

5.   In general, the study concluded that there
was very limited use of governmental patents: about
12.4 percent of the sample group had been applied
commercially, and 2.7 percent had proved quite commercially important.[58]

Sumner Myers Study

One final study will be mentioned, since it
focused explicitly on determining the relative importance of government-funded information in stimulating significant innovation in commercial industry. The study was conducted by Sumner Myers and
his colleagues at the National Planning Association
(NPA) for the National Science Foundation (NSF).
It investigated the origins of 567 "most significant" innovations in three industries: computers,
housing, and railroads.[59] The major findings of
relevance here are the following:

1.   Almost 10 percent of 567 significant innovations originated in federally funded R&D, a little over 7 percent from the three major science
agencies; most of these major science agency ideas
were transferred to the computer industry.[60]

2.   Most of the innovations founded on government R&D were on a larger scale, more innovative
than comparable commercial innovations, and required
a greater development investment than comparable
commercially based innovations.[61]

3.   Almost 54 percent of the 567 innovations
originated from in-house information, and the bal-
ance from external channels, primarily personal

contact. Only 5.8 percent were stimulated by publications.[62]

   4.   Three-fourths of the 567 innovations were
stimulated by a market need, by a new technical
problem, or both. General background information
only rarely stimulated an innovation.[63]

Summary of More General Horizontal
Transfer Studies

   Very little specific item transfer was identified either through a detailed search of the origins of industrial innovation or by examining
government-owned patent/license usage.[64] The DRI
Missile/Space Applications Study did identify a
number of more general areas of technology transfer
or potential transfer.

   Two key methods of transfer were identified:
technologist mobility and new, technically based
spin-off firms. Both methods of transfer were en-
hanced by the government's creation of a market for
many new areas of sophisticated technology.

   The one small experimental transfer program
indicated that a market-oriented, interpersonal
technique could be used to effectuate transfer of
aerospace inventions. The patent studies, on the
other hand, indicated that the grant of a patent or
license motivated little commercial application
either by government contractors or by third party
licensees.

   Both the ADL and the NPA studies indicated
that interpersonal contact was the primary mode of
transfer for externally generated technology, and
both indicated that market-oriented technology was
more likely to stimulate industrial interest and
development than was general background technical
information.

CONCLUSIONS

The three studies of RDC effectiveness indicate that very little identifiable transfer to client companies has resulted from RDC dissemination
programs. These studies provide some additional
data to support the first hypothesis, which predicted that little transfer was to be expected from
the NASA dissemination program.[65] The DRI study of
Tech Brief usage also provides some evidence to
support this hypothesis, in that less than 0.5 percent of the respondents reported any specific
transfer, and only 8 percent considered it important
to their work. The DRI Channels Report indicates
that most technologists in the five industries (all
primarily commercial) sampled do not consider
space/defense technology an important source of new
technology.

The hypothesis concerning the need for a technical impedance match for transfer to be likely
gains some additional support from the findings of
the DRI Tech Brief study, in that the majority of
Tech Brief users were in technically sophisticated
industries; the figure was proportionally higher
than the number of NASA Tech Briefs devoted to
technology useful for these industries. The machinery and machine tool industries, on the other
hand, made relatively little use of Tech Briefs,
despite the large relative number published in
fields of interest to these industries. The results of the DRI Channels Report also provide additional evidence in that use of space/defense
sources of technical information was found to be
highly correlated with the sophistication of the
respondent's industrial group and his familiarity
with space/defense R&D. The high transfer rates
found by Roberts and his colleagues among technically sophisticated spin-off companies further re-
inforces this hypothesis. Peripheral evidence is
provided by the Hayes study, which shows a very
high rate of attempted transfer among electronic
firms, most of which participated heavily in the
space/defense market.

The results of both the Shimshoni and the
Roberts studies generally indicate that small,
technically sophisticated firms have provided an
excellent base for the development and commercial
application of externally generated technology.
The methods of transfer were not technical literature dissemination but technologist mobility and
internal technical entrepreneurship. These two
studies were the only ones found among the comparison studies that focused on small, technically
based companies, but they did not examine the impact of technical literature on transfer.   The
third hypothesis argues that Route 128-type spin-
off firms would provide the most receptive audience
for NASA RDC services. The best that can be said
for additional confirmation of this hypothesis by
the comparison studies is that the Roberts and
Shimshoni studies indicated that small spin-off
firms were quite receptive to externally developed
space/defense technology and have been quite successful at transferring it for commercial application.*

On the other hand, ARAC has been able to maintain a very high renewal rate among a number of
very large corporations which have few of the characteristics of the spin-off firms. Whether this
renewal rate is the result of receptivity to space/
defense technology among these large corporate
clients, or whether they continue to subscribe for
other reasons, is not shown by the comparison
studies.

A number of these studies indicate quite
clearly that specific item transfer is not common

---

*"Commercial application" as used by Roberts
means that the end item use is not connected with
space/defense application at any contractor level.
From conversations with Roberts concering this
matter of definition, it appears that he tried
quite hard to avoid lumping any space/defense end
item use in his commercial diversification figures.

and is hard to identify. The DRI Commercial Applications Study concluded that general area transfer
was more likely than transfer of specific by-
products of space/defense technology. The studies
by ADL, Roberts, and Shimshoni all indicate the importance of internal technical entrepreneurship in
transferring space/defense technology. Of course,
only the ADL study is directly relevant to the
fourth hypothesis, which is concerned with the need
for a transfer agent when externally developed
technology is to be transferred across organizational lines.

The NPA study also adds some data to confirm
the need for a market-oriented approach to transfer
and the importance of interpersonal communication
as a primary method of transferring extra-firm
technical information.

The fifth hypothesis advances the idea that
NASA policies restricting entrepreneurial activities and the NASA-imposed requirement that RDC's
become self-sufficient in three to five years have
tended to retard transfer experimentation and have
limited the RDC role to that of technical librarian.
Both the NERAC and the ARAC reports indicate that
their center activities have been restricted to selective technical information dissemination. The
reports also indicate that neither center felt it
could afford interpersonal transfer experiments or
establishment of effective feedback mechanisms.

These two RDC studies do not show any causal
relation between NASA policies and the rate of
transfer among RDC clients. The other comparison
studies indicate that general background literature
dissemination is not likely to promote transfer
directly, and thus it would appear that NASA policies have not encouraged transfer. However, insufficient time has elapsed to measure fully the impact of these NASA policies on RDC effectiveness.

NOTES

1. See U.S. Congress, House of Representatives, Committee on Science and Astronautics, Subcommittee on Advanced Research and Technology, 1967 NASA Authorization. Hearings, 89th Congress, second session (Washington, D.C.: U.S. GPO, 1966), pp. 642-55. See generally Richard Carpenter's study of technology transfer for U.S. Congress, Senate, Select Committee on Small Business, Subcommittee on Science and Technology, Policy Planning for Technology Transfer. Report, 90th Congress, 1st session, S. Doc. No. 15 (Washington, D.C.: U.S. GPO, May, 1967), pp. 122-24, 146-48, for a discussion of the NASA program. See also U.S. Congress, Senate, Committee on Aeronautical and Space Sciences, Space Program Benefits. Hearings, 91st Congress, second session (Washington, D.C.: U.S. GPO, 1970).

2. 1967 NASA Authorization. Hearings, pp. 645-47.

3. Ibid., p. 647.

4. 1967 NASA Authorization. Hearings, p. 647. Tangible benefit was defined as value equal to or greater than cost.

5. Ibid.

6. ARAC, Final Report, A Study of Information/ Technology Transfer in Industrial Firms, report prepared under NASA contract NSR 15-003-055 (Bloomington, Ind.: ARAC, January 15, 1968); and ARAC, ARAC Technology Transfers, prepared by C. Mullis (Bloomington, Ind.: ARAC, May, 1968) (hereafter cited as Mullis Report).

7. NERAC, An Account of the Activities and Results of the First Year of Operation of the New England Research Application Center, prepared under NASA contract NSR 07-002-029 (Storrs, Conn.: NERAC, March 31, 1968). This report and three short case

studies represent the NERAC study of the transfer
process thus far. The case studies are all basical-
ly descriptive and add no further data for this
study.

    8. See ARAC, Final Report, pp. 4-5. The ARAC
summary presented nine key findings, but only three
appear pertinent for this analysis.

    9. Ibid., pp. 23-24.

    10. See DRI, Channels of Technology Acquisi-
tion in Commercial Firms and the NASA Dissemination
Program, NASA-sponsored report (Springfield, Va.:
CFSTI, June, 1967), p. 29, which found that technologists relied mainly on literature for general
awareness or background information.

    11. Mullis Report, pp. 3-4.

    12. Ibid., pp. 4-13.

    13. In general, the studies of Allen at MIT
indicate that ideas and technical solutions generated within the firm are the most commonly accepted
and are used for most applications. See Thomas
Allen, "The Differential Performance of Information
Channels in the Transfer of Technology," working
paper, Alfred P. Sloan School of Management (Cambridge, Mass.: MIT Sloan School, June, 1966).
        Sumner Myers, in his study of 567 signif-
icant innovations in three industries, found that
35 percent resulted from extra-firm sources, 54
percent from in-house channels, and 11 percent from
multiple channels not separately identifiable.
NPA, "Technology Transfer and Industrial Innovation," unpublished report prepared for NSF by
Sumner Myers, et al. (Washington, D.C.: NSF, February, 1967), pp. 2-10. See also the published
version: Sumner Myers and Donald Marquis, Successful Industrial Innovations, NSF 69-17 (Washington,
D.C.: U.S. GPO, May, 1969).

    14. See NPA, op. cit., pp. 45-50, 95-97.

15. DRI, op. cit., p. 47. Of course, there
was also some variation by functional orientation
of the respondent. Ibid., p. 49. All government
sources checked by DRI contained mainly space/
defense technology.

16. Richard Hayes, "A Study of the Transfer
of Technology from Government Sponsored R&D to
Commercial Operations in Selected Electronic Companies," unpublished doctoral dissertation (Washington, D.C.: American University, 1968). Mr.
Hayes was an employee of NASA during this period
and his research was, in part, sponsored by NASA.
His study is based exclusively on mail question-
aires, supplemented by statistical analysis.

17. Ibid., pp. 212-14.

18. See analysis of federal R&D funding in
Samuel Doctors, The Role of the Federal Agencies in
Technology Transfer (Cambridge, Mass.: The MIT
Press, 1969), Ch. 2, pp. 10-19, for discussion of
this assertion.

19. Hayes, op. cit., p. 220.

20. Ibid., p. 215.

21. Ibid., pp. 220-22. Of course, most of
the larger contractors have direct, free access to
both DOD and NASA data banks, and the study does
not break down the response to RDC services by company size.

22. See Office of Industrial Application,
University of Maryland, Final Report of 1964 Activities and Final Report of 1965 Activities, reports
prepared for NASA (Greenbelt, Md.: Goddard Space
Flight Center, 1965, 1966) for a comprehensive presentation of the results of these two one-year programs.
    When this direct attempt to interest com-
panies in Tech Briefs did not appear very successful, a new program was started which attempted to

follow up requests for NASA technology received by
any of the 13 NASA laboratories or field offices.
A description of this program appears in Office of
Industrial Application, University of Maryland,
Continuing Studies in 1966 and 1967 to Develop Dissemination Procedures for Use with the Technology
Utilization Program and Develop In-Depth Case His-
tories of Commercial Utilization of NASA Technology
Within Industry, Final Report (Greenbelt, Md.:
Goddard Space Flight Center, July 31, 1967). This
latter portion of the program lasted from early
1966 to mid-1967. The study contacted 7,500 companies about their possible utilization of 370 NASA
inventions. The study concluded that NASA technology was being "applied to other sectors of the economy at a rate much faster than many of us realized."
Ibid., p. 216. However, no quantitative data on
this conclusion is provided. For a number of reasons, including a failure to provide quantitative
data, the project was shifted to DRI in late 1967.

23. The process for the collection and evalu-
ation of the new technology that leads to Tech
Briefs is discussed in detail in Doctors, op. cit.,
Ch. 7.

24. See Arthur D. Little, Inc., Technology
Transfer and Technology Utilization Program, report
to the NASA OTU (Washington, D.C.: NASA, January,
1965), p. 5 (hereafter cited as 1965 ADL Report),
for a discussion of this Tech Brief problem.

25. See Ch. 6, section entitled "Implications
of the Findings for the Hypotheses," for a discussion of the reaction of the machinery and machine
tool group to RDC-supplied technical information.

26. Several other recent studies used for
background material for this chapter include AIAA,
Application of Aerospace Technology and Systems
Techniques in Civil Areas (Washington, D.C.: AIAA,
May, 1967); Herbert Kleiman, "The Integrated Cir-
cuit: A Case Study of Product Innovation in the
Electronics Industry," unpublished doctoral

dissertation (Washington, D.C.: School of Business Administration, George Washington University, June, 1966).

Originally I had planned to include the recent Stanford Research Institute study of impact of the space program on six areas of the economy: Vol. I, Aviation and Aeronautics; Vol. II, Science; Vol. III, New Materials Technology; Vol. IV, Public Health, Medicine and Biological Research; Vol. V, Economic Impact on Several Communities; Vol. VI, New Jobs. However, after speaking with the project director, John Meitner, and two members of his staff, and reading the reports, it seems to me that the study is hardly more than a literature search. It provides no new data, and it tends to be biased and self-serving. It has therefore not been included.

See generally Stanford Research Institute, Some Major Impacts of the National Space Program, report prepared for NASA by John Meitner et al. in five parts plus a summary, NASA contract, NASW-1722 (Washington, D.C.: CFSTI, September, 1968). The only portion of this project concerned with industrial transfer used the percentage of NASA-sponsored reports listed in STAR, compared with various other contributors, as a measure of the NASA impact on potential transfer in the materials area. See Vol. IV, ibid.

27. DRI, The Commercial Applications of Missile/Space Technology, NASA-sponsored report (Springfield, Va.: CFSTI, September, 1963).

28. Ibid., p. 1.

29. Ibid., pp. vii-viii.

30. See Donald Marquis, ed., Second Report of the Research Program on the Management of Science and Technology (Cambridge, Mass.: The MIT Sloan School, October, 1967), for a complete listing of NASA-sponsored studies in this area through October, 1967.

31. The studies were performed by Roberts and a number of his colleagues and graduate students. The results have been presented in a number of reports and unpublished theses, but no comprehensive/ book has yet been put together. An abbreviated summary of Roberts' work appeared in April, 1969: "Entrepreneurship and Technology," in Donald Marquis and William Gruber, eds., Factors in the Transfer of Technology (Cambridge: The MIT Press, 1969), pp. 219-37.

32. Ibid., p. 225.

33. See Daniel Shimshoni, "Aspects of Scientific Entrepreneurship," unpublished doctoral dissertation (Cambridge, Mass.: Kennedy School of Government, Harvard University, May, 1966).

34. Some initial work was performed during late 1964, but most of the work was performed in 1965. The project is described in two ADL reports: 1965 ADL Report, pp. 2-17; and Technology Transfer and the Technology Utilization Program, report to the NASA OTU (Washington, D.C.: NASA, April, 1966), pp. 7-17 (hereafter cited as 1966 ADL Report).

35. See 1966 ADL Report, p. 8.

36. The ADL findings are, of course, based on a small sample of specific item transfers. However, the same group of consultants working on this small experimental project had worked on numerous other NASA OTU projects and on various industrial innovation studies conducted at ADL in the early 1960's. Thus, these results cannot be viewed in isolation from the other ADL transfer and innovation studies. See for example, ADL, Patterns and Problems of Technical Innovation in American Industry, report to NSF (Washington, D.C.: CFSTI, 1963).

37. Exclusive licenses have only rarely been granted by federal agencies. See Doctors, op. cit., pp. 146-55 for a discussion of government licensing policy.

38.   See the list of fifteen patent practice
reports of government agencies in Federal Council
for Science and Technology, Annual Report on Government Patent Policy (Washington, D.C.:   U.S. GPO,
June, 1966).

39.   See ibid., pp. 46-47 for a list of twenty-
three hearings on federal patent policy held between 1958 and 1966 by three different Congressional
committees.

40.   See, for example, the statements of Sena-
tors Russell Long and Wayne Morse in 1965 hearings.
U.S. Congress, Senate, Committee on the Judiciary,
Subcommittee on Patents, Trademarks and Copyrights,
Government Patent Policy. Hearings, 89th Congress,
first session, S. 789, S. 1809, and S. 1899 (Washington, D.C.:   U.S. GPO, June, 1965), Pt. 1, pp.
328-50, Pt. 2, pp. 547-93.

41.   See, for example, U.S. Congress, House of
Representatives, Committee on Science and Astronau-
tics, Subcommittee on Patents and Scientific Inven-
tions, Ownership of Inventions Developed in the
Course of Federal Space Research Contracts, Report,
87th Congress, second session (Washington, D.C.:
U.S. GPO, April, 1962) (committee print); Helge
Holst, "Government Patent Policy--Its Impact on
Contractor Cooperation with the Government and
Widespread Use of Government Sponsored Technology,"
Patent, Trademark, and Copyright Journal of Re-
search and Education, IX, 2 (Summer, 1965), 273-96.

42.   See Chalmers Sherwin and Raymond Isenson,
"First Interim Report on Project Hindsight," report
to the Director of Defense Research and Engineering
(Washington, D.C.:   DOD, June, 1966; revised October, 1966); and Doctors, op. cit., Ch. 2, pp. 10-19.

43.   Donald Watson and Mary Holman, "Evaluation of NASA's Patent Policies" (Washington, D.C.:
George Washington University, Department of Economics, 1966).

44. Harbridge House, Inc., Government Patent
Policy Study, report prepared for Federal Council
on Science and Technology, Committee on Government
Patent Policy, Vols. I-IV (Washington, D.C.: U.S.
GPO, May, 1968).

45. See Court of Claims, Patent Cases Act of
1948, 28 U.S.C.A. 1948 (as amended 1960) and interpretation in Herbert Cooper Co., unpublished division of the Comptroller General, B-136916 (August
25, 1958). An excellent article discussing the
rights of patent/license holders in government contracting bidding is Gerald Mosinghoff and Robert
Allnutt, "Patent Infringement in Government Procurement: A Remedy Without a Right?," Notre Dame Law
Review, XLII (October, 1966), 5-28.

46. See Doctors, op. cit., pp. 134-37.

47. Measurement of utilization rates for government-sponsored patents has yielded results which
have ranged between 7 and 13 percent. See Donald
Watson, Harold Bright, and Arthur Burns, "Federal
Patent Policy in Contracts for Research and Development," Patent, Trademark, and Copyright Journal
of Research and Education, IV, 4 (Winter, 1960),
342, estimating a 13 percent utilization rate;
U.S. Congress, Senate, Committee on the Judiciary,
Subcommittee on Patents, Trademarks, and Copyrights,
Patent Practices of the Department of Defense. Report (Washington, D.C.: U.S. GPO, September, 1961),
p. 35 (committee print), estimating a 7 percent
utilization rate; and Mary Holman, "Government Research and Development Inventions--A New Resource?,"
Land Economics, XLI (August, 1965), 231-38, estimating a 10 percent utilization rate.
          These utilization rate measurements must
be compared with a 60 percent utilization rate
found for commercially developed patents. Consid-
ering the fact that defense contractors patent at
10 percent of the rate of comparable commercial
firms, this means an equivalent usage rate of 1/60
for government-sponsored inventions. See Berkev
Sanders, "Patterns of Commercial Exploitation of

Patented Inventions by Large and Small Companies,"
<u>Patent, Trademark, and Copyright Journal of Re-
search and Education</u>, VIII, 1 (Spring, 1964), 51-93,
indicating a 60 percent utilization rate for commercially developed patents.

48. Watson and Holman, <u>op. cit</u>., pp. 13-14,
69-70.

49. Contractors petitioned for waiver for
about 5 percent of their disclosed inventions.
Doctors, <u>op. cit</u>., Ch. 10, note 29.

50. <u>Ibid</u>., p. 139.

51. Ninety-seven different companies held 107
non-exclusive licenses to forty-seven patents, or
about 10.1 percent of NASA's patent portfolio, and
one exclusive license had been awarded. Watson and
Holman, <u>op. cit</u>., pp. 65-79.

52. Harbridge House, <u>op. cit</u>., pp. iii-iv,
I-7.

53. <u>Ibid</u>., p. v.

54. <u>Ibid</u>. Also see Doctors, <u>op. cit</u>., Ch. 2,
pp. 10-19, for federal R&D funding figures.

55. Harbridge House, <u>loc. cit</u>.

56. <u>Ibid</u>.

57. <u>Ibid</u>.

58. <u>Ibid</u>., p. I-6.

59. NPA, <u>op. cit</u>. See also the final published version of this report, Myers and Marquis,
<u>op. cit</u>.

60. NPA, <u>op. cit</u>., p. V-24.

61. <u>Ibid</u>., pp. V-28 to V-30.

62. *Ibid*., pp. V-9 to V-12.

63. *Ibid*., p. V-40.

64. This conclusion is, of course, based on studies completed in the early and mid-1960's. Thus, they may not account for the impetus to transfer provided by the greatly expanded federal R&D program in the late 1950's and early 1960's. Given an average innovation diffusion rate of seventeen to twenty years, the results of these patent utilization studies may be quite unrealistic. See a more detailed discussion of this problem in Doctors, *op. cit*. See also U.S. Congress, House of Representatives, Committee on Science and Astronautics, For the Benefit of All Mankind. Report, 91st Congress, second session (Washington, D.C.: U.S. GPO, September 14, 1970); and U.S. Congress, Senate, Committee on Aeronautical and Space Sciences, *op. cit*.

65. The five hypotheses investigated during the field study are presented in Ch. 3, section entitled "Field Study Hypotheses."

3

TECHNOLOGY TRANSFER:
PURPOSE, PROCESS,
AND SOME HYPOTHESES

PURPOSE

Transfer of aerospace technology to commercial industry has been widely advertised as an integral and necessary result of the public investment in space R&D. To assist this transfer and to measure the results, NASA established the TUP in early 1962.[1] The initial program was largely limited to a centralized literature dissemination program and some promotion in the trade press.* When this centralized dissemination effort bore little in the way of measurable transfer results, NASA decided to establish a number of university-based RDC's to act as decentralized transfer agents. For the purposes of this study, transfer and dissemination are not

----

*Some initial transfer activity at the Midwest Research Institute was funded early in the program. This work was aimed at making NASA technology available to Midwestern industry, but this was only a small pilot program. It consisted primarily of a mobile exhibit of NASA technology which was displayed at various industrial centers throughout the Midwest.

synonymous terms.[2] The former implies active participation by both transferor and transferee and
requires creative adaptation of the technology for
the new institutional application. Dissemination,
on the other hand, is a more passive process requiring primarily physical movement of technology
from one institutional setting to another (no creative adaptation need be involved, nor need the
transferee intend to incorporate the new technology
into his ongoing work product). Some receptivity
must be present for the communication to occur. Of
course, communication of technical information is
part of the transfer process; but without more than
selective dissemination, the probability of transfer is not high.

The first of the RDC's was established in
early 1962 and the last, at the University of Connecticut, in March, 1967. These centers were to
make NASA-furnished aerospace technology available
to industrial clients for a fee.[3] Originally they
were largely subsidized by NASA, but within three
to five years client fees were to be raised to cover all out-of-pocket costs.[4]

List of RDC's and Their Dates
of Establishment[5]

Midwest Research Institute (now closed)	January, 1962
Indiana University (partially closed)	January, 1963
Wayne State University (now closed)	January, 1964
Southeastern State College	February, 1964
University of Maryland (closed July, 1967)	April, 1964
University of Pittsburgh	May, 1964
North Carolina Science & Technology Research Center	June, 1964
University of New Mexico	May, 1965
University of Southern California	January, 1967
University of Connecticut	April, 1967

The purpose of the field study portion of this volume was to investigate the effectiveness of these centers in transferring space/defense technology to commercial/industrial firms.* NASA has advertised these centers as "experimental transfer programs,"[6] but in practice their main function has been to disseminate space/defense literature in packages tailored to client requests for technical information dissemination as a mechanism for motivating interest and subsequent use of aerospace technology by commercial industry.

The study used the fifty-four industrial clients of NERAC, the NASA RDC for New England, as its primary sample. A secondary sample was composed of the sixty client firms of ARAC, located at the University of Indiana. (See Appendix A.) One non-profit corporation, the MIT Lincoln Laboratory, was included in the sample. There were other non-profit users, such as the University of Connecticut researchers and the Connecticut Development Commission, but they were not included in the primary sample. Similarly, a number of non-profit educational and governmental institutions were among the ARAC clientele but were not included in the total sample.

The sampling method used for the NERAC portion was in-depth personal interviews; mail questionnaires were used for sampling the transfer experience of ARAC clients. (See Appendix B.) Since some ARAC firms were reluctant to supply written information in several sensitive areas, such as sales or R&D figures for divisions, and because there was no opportunity for probing the questionnaire responses through personal interviews, this

---

*Space/defense and aerospace technology are used interchangeably in this study and are meant to refer to the part of the R&D work product of federal R&D programs generally available to the RDC's as their major data base. Any technology related to missile or aerospace developments is included.

secondary sample was used primarily to provide general back-up data for the findings of the primary sample, which was based primarily on personal interviews. (A detailed discussion of research study design and a presentation of the findings is given in Chapters 5 and 6.)

The focus of the field study was on the transfer of specific items of technology.* However, some attention was given to more general technology transfer, as in some cases where NERAC-supplied information was used as a general background for technical problem solving or as part of the background material for new product planning.

The field study sought to identify specifically what kinds of companies make use of RDC-supplied space/defense technology, the purposes for which they use this technology, and whether the present RDC programs and policies are effective in promoting the use of aerospace technology in non-aerospace firms or in aerospace firms for non-aerospace applications.

PROCESS

This study is primarily concerned with horizontal technology transfer, that is, the process

---

*Specific item transfer is defined for this study as the transfer of a specific item of technology such that it is incorporated in the work product of some individual (or individuals) and such that it can be readily identified and a dollar value can be placed on its contribution to some end item of this work product. The specific item must be tangible and must be such that it would generally fit the common-sense definition of an invention. Of course, the item is typically transferred in written or oral form, not as a specific item of hardware.

whereby technology developed in one institutional
setting is adapted for use in another. Any transfer, whether horizontal, from space/defense R&D to
commercial industry, or vertical, within one institutional setting, requires certain elements:[7]

1. An invention or some new area of technology

2. Incorporation of the invention or new technology in an innovation

3. A difference between the context of the
invention and the context in which it is incorporated in an innovation

4. A communication or linking process which
brings the incorporation about.

Of course, these various elements usually occur over a relatively long time period, and the new
technology may or may not be embodied in some specific item of hardware. Transfer may occur by
simple imitation, e.g., hybrid corn. A different
type of transfer occurs when someone notes the sim-
ilarity of a principle between one application and
another, e.g., when the deposition process used in
the nuclear rocket program was found to provide a
smoother-smoking pipe bowl or when a micrometeorite
detector is found applicable to the detection of
heartbeats in a chick embryo. This type of transfer by analogy is a more complex process, requiring
that the technology be adapted for its secondary
application in a quite different environment.

These are the elements of the transfer process,
whether horizontal or vertical. The rate at which
they become operable may, however, be quite different in the two types of transfer.[8] Most of the
major studies done thus far on technological diffusion rates have been directed primarily at vertical
transfer, and have concluded that the rate of diffusion from invention to adoption by a substantial
portion of an industry averages almost twenty years.
There is, of course, considerable variability in

the rate of diffusion for any given invention, and
this rate appears to be a function of a number of
interrelated variables, including the nature of the
invention, the structure of the industry, the char-
acter of the innovator, and market demand.

Studies investigating the transfer process
have tended to conclude that five general characteristics of the invention or new area of technology will determine the rate of transfer:[9]

1.   The ease with which economic advantages
relative to existing technology may be perceived

2.   The transfer time's being directly propor-
tional to complexity

3.   The ease of communication between the inventor and/or transfer agent and the innovator

4.   The divisibility of the new technology,
permitting its trial on a limited scale

5.   The compatibility of the innovation with
existing technology and with existing ideas and
values.

Many of the inherent characteristics of an
aerospace invention or new area of technology may
tend to retard its rate of transfer, since this
type of technology has impediments not found in
most commercial inventions. One of the characteristics is that most aerospace technology is oriented toward performance, not cost, and it may therefore be harder to perceive immediate economic advantages in commercial application. Furthermore,
aerospace technology is generally quite complex and
more technically sophisticated than most commercial
technology and is perceived in this way by businessmen. Also, there appears to be relatively little
interaction between the aerospace industry and commercial industry, even within the same corporate

framework.* Also, it appears that space/defense
technology that is transferred is on a larger scale
and requires a greater investment than comparable
commercially developed inventions.[10] Last, space/
defense technology may be more innovative and may
generally be less compatible with existing production technology.[11]

Besides these generally acknowledged invention
characteristics affecting the rate of diffusion,
additional factors appear to affect the rate of
transfer substantially. For example, a champion
(technical entrepreneur) is typically required for
radical new inventions, or the inventions will
languish. An individual must take the role of
entrepreneur, assume the risks of failure, and actively promote the invention, circumventing recog-
nized channels of information and authority.[12]
This factor applies mainly to specific item transfer. For transfer in general, we note that transfer of aerospace technology seems to follow a hierarchical pattern requiring a technical impedance
match between the sophistication of the information
and that of the transferor.[13] Also, there is likely to be less organizational receptivity in such
industrial areas as textiles, machine tools, and
shoe machinery, since innovation in these industries

---

*Very little hard data to validate this lack
of communication exists, but several researchers
have indicated that there appears to be a gap in
communications between the space/defense sector of
the economy and the commercial industrial sector.
See Robert Solo, "Gearing Military R&D to Economic
Growth," Harvard Business Review, XL, 6 (November-
December, 1962), 49-60; Merton Peck and Frederick
Scherer, The Weapons Acquisition Process: An Eco-
nomic Analysis (Boston: Division of Research,
Graduate School of Business Administration, Harvard
University, 1962), p. 130.

appears to occur mainly by invasion from newer,
more dynamic industries, such as electronics and
chemicals.[14] Perception by the transferee of the
relevance of governmental technology for his business is an important variable affecting initial receptivity and use of government R&D-originated inventions.* Furthermore, transfer is more likely to
be stimulated by new technology that is addressed
to the solution of a specific problem, i.e., need-
oriented, not means-oriented.[15]

Two studies indicate that technical information
that stimulated innovations was primarily need-
oriented, i.e., it was used in the solution of an
already formulated problem. In about 75 percent of
the innovations investigated by these two studies,
technical information played a passive role in assisting in the solution of already given problems,
while in about 25 percent of the cases new technical information played an active role, i.e., led to
the exploration of hitherto unthought-of areas of
application. Finally, space/defense technology is
typically less concerned with short-term, commercially useful technology, whereas a three-year (or
less) payoff is typical of most commercial R&D.[16]

Each of these additional factors created a
problem for the horizontal transfer of space/defense
technology to commercial industry. In the horizontal transfer of aerospace technology, it may be
necessary for the transfer agent to act as a champion until a champion is identified in the transferor organization.[17] Also, the most likely

_____

*Generally, interviews conducted in conjunction
with Samuel Doctors, The Role of the Federal Agencies in Technology Transfer (Cambridge, Mass.: The
MIT Press, 1969), indicated that businessmen and
technologists in most commercial industrial firms
in Massachusetts do not consider space/defense
technology relevant for their near-term new technology needs.

technical sophistication match for aerospace technology transfer is not apt to lie in a commercial
industrial firm (particularly a consumer product
firm), since most commercial R&D is further down
the hierarchical chain, further away from scientific
theory and government R&D application, and nearer
to commercial technology sophistication levels.[18]
Furthermore, political constraints may require that
government transfer activity be centered in areas
of the country containing a poor industrial impedance match for sophisticated space/defense technology.*

Recent studies of commercial firm usage of government sources of technical information and of
usage of government patents or licenses point to
still another problem: most commercial firms do
not perceive government sources of technical information or government patents or licenses as an important source of new technology.[19] A study by DRI
which surveyed segments of five commercial industries concluded that government sources of technology are not generally viewed as an important source
of new technology. Also, the activities of government transfer programs such as the NASA TUP or CFSTI
or STS programs have been oriented primarily to
providing general background information, mainly in
the form of science agency project reports. None
of these federal programs has yet been oriented to
providing information packaged to solve present
commercial problems. Thus, aerospace technology by
its very nature and institutional setting provides
a unique set of problems which may slow the rate of
transfer beyond that common for commercially developed technology. Very little information has been
gathered on the rate and direction of horizontal

---

*Much of the NASA transfer program has been
centered in the Midwest and Southwest and, more important, the NASA TUP has been committed to a program which emphasizes transfer to industrial firms
having little contact with space technology.

transfer, but we do know that the process of technology transfer from federal R&D to commercial use
is exceedingly complex and provides a setting for
the study of the transfer process far different
from those typically investigated by rural sociolo-
gists and industrial economists.

FIELD STUDY HYPOTHESES

In the course of developing the hypotheses, it
became clear that horizontal transfer, both specific item and general area, would be difficult to de-
tect, since transfer tends to be a subtle, complex
phenomenon, often requiring a number of intermediate
steps before the new technical information is integrated into the ongoing work product of company
personnel.[20] The process typically requires the
recognition of a need, the perception that some new
item of technology satisfies that need, and the in-
tegration of that technology into some ongoing organizational framework, including test, evaluation,
and ultimate diffusion to the market. A given item
of new technology may itself prove of little value,
but it may suggest a different approach to the
problem or stimulate the technologist to look outside his immediate organizational context; and it
may be only one step leading to an ultimate transfer of technology, a catalyst or link in an exceedingly complex chain of events.

Within this general framework of technology
transfer, the field study therefore focused on a
portion of the transfer process which could be explored in the context of the NASA RDC system.

The hypotheses that have been investigated are
the following:

1. It is unlikely that much transfer has occurred as a result of the NASA dissemination program.[21] Technology transfer is a slow process and
the NASA TUP has been in existence for a relatively
short time (since 1962). Industrial diffusion of

new areas of technology appears to average about
seventeen years from the point of initial concep-
tion to adoption by any substantial portion of an
industry. From the discussion of some of the problems presented by the nature of the aerospace technology, it appears that even this average seventeen-
year figure may be low for space/defense technology
transfer.

Several studies have concluded that it is
quite difficult to trace the impact of space/defense
fallout or spin-off on industrial productivity.
The original DRI research project attempted to measure spin-off or by-product transfer from missile/
space R&D programs to commercial industry and concluded that it was extremely difficult, if not im-
possible, at that time (1963) to trace specific
item transfers, bound up as they were with bits and
pieces of technology drawn from a variety of other
sources.

2. Transfer of space/defense technology to
private industry is likely to occur only where the
company has a highly sophisticated technical base.
Measures of such a highly sophisticated technical
base would include the ratio of technologists to
all employees, the types of products and/or services produced by the company, and the amount of
R&D performed by the company as a percentage of
sales. The amount of government-sponsored R&D is
also some indication of technical sophistication of
the company. Since the duration of the NASA RDC
program has been so short, use of and interest in
aerospace technology may provide some indication of
transfer potential even if explicit transfers cannot yet be identified.

3. It is likely that smaller, technically
based firms such as the Boston Route 128 spin-off
firms, have more readily accepted and used the services of the NASA RDC's. Such firms appear to be
more receptive to sophisticated new technology
originating outside the company. As a practical
matter, they often lack the resources for extensive

technical library facilities, and they generally
have more difficulty in obtaining government documents than their larger peers.[22] Also, such firms
often work in technical areas that are similar to
those represented by the NASA RDC technical data
base, thus providing a technical impedance match
for RDC-supplied information. They often use
space/defense technology for both their government
contracts and for commercial application.

4. The transfer of general technical information is more likely than that of specific inventions. The NASA RDC's do not provide an entrepreneurial, market-oriented approach to transfer, and
they generally provide only selective technical
document (or abstract) dissemination, based on literature search strategies developed primarily
through written correspondence or telephone communication. Little effort is made to tailor an invention for transfer to a client company by determining specific company needs for new products, or
by identifying a champion within the company who is
interested in and capable of promoting intra-company
utilization.

5. NASA policies curbing entrepreneurial activities and requiring self-sufficiency within
three to five years have had the effect of inhibiting meaningful transfer experiments. This has been
a difficult hypothesis to establish with direct
field study data, but certain characteristics of
the transfer process make it a highly appealing
hypothesis and important in explaining some of the
negative results of the NASA RDC efforts found by
the field study and the lack of useful feedback
data for future transfer programs that has emanated
from the NASA program to date. To establish this
hypothesis, two subsidiary propositions will be established: (1) NASA policies inhibiting entrepreneurial activities and requiring self-sufficiency
within three to five years have largely restricted
RDC information diffusion efforts to routinized
channels within client companies, such as libraries
or technical information centers; (2) restricting

information channels within client companies has had
the effect of inhibiting useful transfer experiments.

NOTES

1. See Samuel Doctors, <u>The Role of the Federal
Agencies in Technology Transfer</u> (Cambridge, Mass.:
The MIT Press, 1969), Ch. 6, pp. 61-73, which pro-
vides a more detailed history of the TUP and earlier
NASA transfer activities.

2. See <u>ibid</u>., pp. 1-2, for a more detailed
analysis of the terms. In the NASA TUP, the two
concepts are often confused, as when the RDC's are
referred to as "transfer agents" or the dissemination program is referred to as a "technology transfer program."

3. See NASA, <u>The Technology Utilization Program Review</u> (Washington, D.C.: NASA TUP, February,
1967) and U.S. Congress, House of Representatives,
Committee on Science and Astronautics, Subcommittee
on Advanced Research and Technology, <u>1970 NASA Authorization. Hearings</u>, 91st Congress, first session (Washington, D.C.: U.S. GPO, 1969), pp. 720-22.

4. See NASA, <u>op. cit</u>., p. 22, for an official
statement concerning the obligation of RDC's to become self-supporting; and <u>1970 NASA Authorization</u>.
<u>Hearings</u>, pp. 720-21.

5. NASA OTU.

6. See any discussion of the TUP in Congressional NASA Authorization Hearings, 1964 to the
present, for a discussion of the RDC's as "experimental transfer programs or agents."

7. See Richard Rosenbloom, <u>Technology Trans-
fer--Process and Policy . . .</u>, Special Report No.
62 (Washington, D.C.: NPA, July, 1965), p. 9.

8. See Doctors, <u>op. cit</u>., Ch. 3; and Edwin
Mansfield, <u>The Economics of Technological Change</u>

(New York: W. W. Norton, 1968), pp. 97-133, for more detailed discussion of diffusion rates.

9. See Everett Rodgers, <u>Diffusion of Innovation</u> (New York: The Free Press of Glencoe, 1962), pp. 303-05; and Mansfield, <u>op. cit.</u>, pp. 119-33.

10. NPA, "Technology Transfer and Industrial Innovation," unpublished report prepared for NSF by Sumner Myers, <u>et al</u>. (Washington, D.C.: NPA, February, 1967), pp. V-28, V-29. See also the published version: Sumner Myers and Donald Marquis, <u>Successful Industrial Innovations</u>, NSF 69-17 (Washington, D.C.: U.S. GPO, May, 1969).

11. NPA, <u>op. cit.</u>, pp. V-37 to V-38.

12. Donald Schon, <u>Technology and Change</u> (New York: Delacorte Press, 1967), pp. 115-19. Both Roberts and Shimshoni have shown that the technical entrepreneur is a crucial element for technology transfer to such sophisticated industries as electronics and instrumentation: Edward Roberts, "Enpreneurship and Technology," in Donald Marquis and William Gruber, eds., <u>Factors in the Transfer of Technology</u> (Cambridge: Mass.: The MIT Press, 1969), pp. 219-37; and Daniel Shimshoni, "Aspects of Scientific Entrepreneurship," unpublished doctoral dissertation (Kennedy School of Government, Harvard University, May, 1966).

13. See Doctors, <u>op. cit.</u>, Ch. 4, for a discussion of this hierarchical transfer mode.

14. Schon, <u>op. cit.</u>, pp. 159-71.

15. See NPA, <u>op. cit.</u>, pp. V-17 to V-21; see also the study of thirty-two innovations in the scientific instrument industry by James Utterback, "The Process of Technical Innovation in Instrument Firms," unpublished doctoral dissertation (MIT Sloan School, January, 1969).

16. See Robert Solo, "Gearing Military R&D to Economic Growth," <u>Harvard Business Review</u>, XL, 6

(November-December, 1962), 49-60; and U.S. Congress,
House of Representatives, Select Committee on Government Research (the Elliott Committee), Hearings
(Washington, D.C.: U.S. GPO, 1964) for discussion
of this problem.

17. See discussion of need for RDC to supply
a champion until one can be identified in commercial industrial client in Doctors, op. cit., Ch. 8,
pp. 105-10.

18. Ibid., Ch. 4, argues for a hierarchical
model for transfer in the space/defense context.
Clearly such space/defense-originated technology as
solid-state electronics and jet aircraft followed a
generally hierarchical transfer route from basic
scientific discovery to application in the space/
defense market to ultimate transfer to the commercial market. See also Illinois Institute of Technology Research Institute, Technology in Retrospect
and Critical Events in Science, report prepared for
NSF (Washington, D.C.: NSF, December, 1968).

19. DRI, Channels of Technology Acquisition
in Commercial Firms and the NASA Dissemination Program, NASA-sponsored report (Springfield, Va.:
CFSTI, June, 1967), pp. 2, 45-80. In the patent/
license area two studies indicate that neither
space/defense contractors nor third party licensees
view government inventions of great commercial value. See Donald Watson and Mary Holman, "Evaluation
of NASA's Patent Policies" (Washington, D.C.: Department of Economics, George Washington University,
1966); and Harbridge House, Inc., Government Patent
Policy Study, Vol. I (Washington, D.C.: U.S. GPO,
May, 1968). The latter report covers the patent/
license experiences of all major government agencies except NASA. See Chapter 2, pp. 34-39, for an
analysis of the findings of these studies.

20. NPA, op. cit., pp. V-39 to V-40. One of
the major conclusions of this study was that prob-
lem- or need-oriented new technology was three
times as likely to stimulate an innovation as was
general background information not oriented to

commercial needs. No attempt is made to screen
technology for actual commercial needs or present
technical problems.

21. NPA, "The Impact of the U.S. Civilian
Space Program on the U.S. Domestic Economy," report
prepared for the Lockheed Aircraft Corporation
(Washington, D.C.: NPA, July, 1965); ADL, Transfer
of Aerospace Technology in the United States--A
Critical Review, report to the Plowden Committee,
U.K. (Cambridge, Mass.: ADL, July, 1966). See
also DRI, The Commercial Application of Missile/
Space Technology (Springfield, Va.: CFSTI, Septem-
ber, 1963), pp. vii-viii, 1-25.

22. See Donald Schon, "Champions for Radical
New Inventions," Harvard Business Review, XLI, 2
(March-April, 1963), 77-86; Elting Morison, "A Case
of Innovation," Engineering and Science Monthly
(April, 1950), 5-11; Rodgers, op. cit., p. 304, for
a discussion of innovators' use of informal channels of information, often bypassing the usual
means of obtaining new information.

4

MAJOR SCIENCE AGENCY R&D TRANSFER POLICIES

In the United States a large portion of all
R&D activity is supported by federal expenditure,
but much of the work is actually performed by private industry.[1] Most of this R&D expenditure is
for space/defense programs; often these programs
are highly specialized and incorporate very advanced technology.[2] In 1968 (the last year for
which National Science Foundation [NSF] figures on
industrial R&D spending were available at the time
of this study) the federal government supported
between 60 and 70 percent of all R&D spending in
the industrial sector, depending on whether overhead R&D funding is allocated to federal or private
corporate sources and on whether federal spending on
capital facilities is included. The work product
of this vast R&D expenditure is oriented toward
quality and performance, not cost. Much of this
technology may have little immediate relevance for
civilian industrial application. However, studies
such as that of Sumner Myers for NSF and those of
Donald Marquis, Edward Roberts, and their colleagues
at MIT, seem to indicate that transfer to civilian
industry does occur in measurable quantities.[3]
Myers' results indicate that almost 10 percent of

the "significant" innovations (56 of 567) in the
three sampled industries--housing, computers and
railroads--resulted from government-funded information. The results of the Marquis/Roberts four-year
project at MIT, sponsored in part by NASA, have resulted in a large number of working papers, theses,
and published materials, some of them cited in various portions of this study. The results of interest here are those performed under the direction of
Roberts. The studies showed that 226 companies
forming the sample of Boston Route 128 spin-off
firms had averaged 40 percent diversification into
the commercial market within five years of their
founding.

What we do not know is how various government
agency policies concerning the acquisition, evaluation, dissemination, and control of legal rights to
intellectual property affect the transfer process,
and whether in fact present policies are effective,
ineffective, or neutral relative to the transfer
process. Clearly, transfer is only a secondary
mission requirement for the three major applied
science agencies--the Department of Defense (DOD),
the Atomic Energy Commission (AEC), and the National Aeronautics and Space Administration (NASA)--
but since these three agencies control, directly or
indirectly, over 60 percent of all R&D conducted in
this country, they have some responsibility for
promoting the secondary application of their R&D
results.

Each of these three agencies has adopted policies designed in varying degrees to promote this
secondary application. DOD seeks to encourage
transfer directly through its contractors by promoting their exclusive rights to much of their R&D
work product. To accomplish this end, DOD enforces
a strict "need to know" requirement for the transfer of any technical data considered by its contractors to be proprietary. DOD is also quite
liberal in granting contractors title to their patentable inventions (for commercial application).
In addition, DOD, through its extensive overhead

funding of independent contractor R&D programs,
provides a further means for the contractor to obtain edclusive rights to much of his own most advanced technology. DOD conducts no programs of its
own to assist civilian industry in utilizing DOD-
developed technology, aside from nominal contribu-
tions to the Department of Commerce CFSTI data bank
and the NASA Scientific and Technical Information
Division (STID) data bank.[4]

The AEC has been concerned almost from its inception with the civilian application of nuclear
R&D results. The AEC environment for transfer,
however, differs from that of DOD and NASA in that
the government, in the person of the AEC, was the
originator and sponsor of nearly all the relevant
technology. Also, there has always been great concern to maintain governmental control over the direction of nuclear application, as indicated by the
enabling act requirements that the AEC retain title
to all patentable nuclear inventions.[5] The AEC has,
however, encouraged civilian applications of nuclear technology in a variety of ways, including
direct subsidy of much of the early application
work in radioisotopes and atomic power. The AEC
has also established an extensive technology dissemination program, including the recently established Industrial Cooperation Program, which provides direct industry contact with two AEC laboratories and related industry, and a joint Tech Brief
program with NASA.[6]

NASA, like DOD, seeks to promote direct transfer through commercialization by its contractors.
But, unlike DOD, NASA maintains an extensive transfer program, TUP, designed to promote transfer to
third parties in civilian industry. This program
represents the first attempt by a major science
agency to establish an integrated technology transfer program, combining an acquisition/evaluation
system, a number of dissemination mechanisms, and
an extensive set of patent/license regulations intended to optimize both the contractor's incentive
to commercialize his own R&D work product and that

of third parties in commercial industry to transfer
NASA-developed technology to commercial application.[7]

Thus, the major science agencies have adopted
quite different policies to effect transfer. This
portion of the study indicates only briefly the di-
vergent, and at times conflicting, approaches taken
by these three agencies. Other federal agencies
also maintain transfer programs of various types
and sizes.[8]

THE NASA TRANSFER PROGRAM

Until early 1971 the extensive NASA transfer
program was under the functional direction of the
Assistant Administrator for Technology Utilization
(TU) who reported to the Deputy Administrator for
Administration.* Now the transfer program is under
the direction of the Assistant Administrator for
Industry Affairs and Technology Utilization. The
dissemination activity remains functionally under
the control of the Office of Technology Utilization
(OTU), one of three offices reporting to the

---

*Initially, the Assistant Administrator for TU
reported directly to the NASA Administrator's office, but a change in 1967 placed TU under the administrative (not technical) organization of NASA.
See Samuel Doctors, The Role of the Federal Agencies in Technology Transfer (Cambridge, Mass.: The
MIT Press, 1969), Ch. 6, pp. 62-63 for a discussion
of the effect of this organizational change on TU
program effectiveness. A new change in the TU
organization in 1971 separated the TUD from the
Scientific Information Division and further down-
graded the transfer function by eliminating the
Assistant Administrator for Technology Utilization.
TUD is now one division reporting to an Assistant
Administrator for Industry Affairs and Technology
Utilization.

Assistant Administrator for TU. The other major
division was the Scientific and Technical Information Division (STID), which now also reports to the
Assistant Administrator for Industry Affairs and TU.
Figures 1 and 2 provide organization charts of the
TUP both before and after the 1961 changes. The
bulk of the research for this study was performed
while the TUP was organized as shown in Figure 1.

STID performs a function similar to that performed for DOD by the Defense Documentation Center
(DDC), namely, that of technical librarian for NASA
and its contractors. While TUD is functionally re-
sponsible for transfer activities including the acquisition, evaluation and dissemination of commercially useful NASA technology.[9] STID collects
technical reports not only from NASA contractors
but also from other government agencies (mainly DOD
and AEC) and domestic and foreign technical literature. Most of these more than 700,000 technical
literature items have been listed on magnetic tapes,
and microfilms of the entire documents have been
prepared.[10]

One of the major themes of the NASA transfer
program is the publication and dissemination of a
wide variety of technical reports, manuals, journal
articles, translations, invention reports (Tech
Briefs), and a wide variety of other, assorted
aerospace-related materials. Technical reports and
documents include technical notes, memoranda,
translations, contractor reports, and such special
publications as conference proceedings, monographs,
data compilations, handbooks, sourcebooks, and
bibliographies. Also in this category are Technology Utilization Reports, Notes, Compilations, Surveys, and Tech Briefs.* Under publications, abstracts, and bibliographies, NASA publishes

----

*The Reports, Notes, Compilations, and Tech
Briefs are specially prepared for TUD purposes,
i.e., for commercial application.

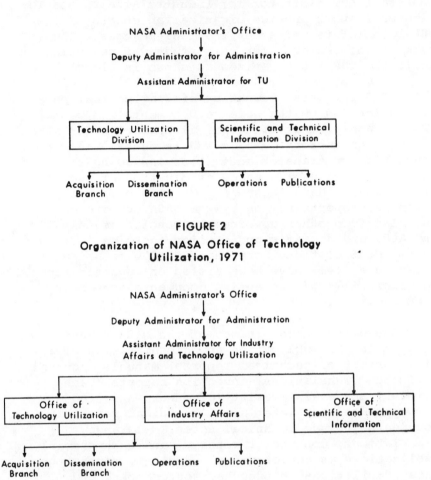

FIGURE 1

Organization of NASA Office of Technology Utilization, 1967-70

NASA Administrator's Office

Deputy Administrator for Administration

Assistant Administrator for TU

Technology Utilization Division

Scientific and Technical Information Division

Acquisition Branch   Dissemination Branch   Operations   Publications

FIGURE 2

Organization of NASA Office of Technology Utilization, 1971

NASA Administrator's Office

Deputy Administrator for Administration

Assistant Administrator for Industry Affairs and Technology Utilization

Office of Technology Utilization

Office of Industry Affairs

Office of Scientific and Technical Information

Acquisition Branch   Dissemination Branch   Operations   Publications

Note: This is not a complete organization chart of NASA, but shows only the offices and positions in the OTU's chain of command.

Source: NASA office of Technology Utilization (OTU)

Scientific and Technical Aerospace Reports (STAR)
and continuing bibliographies on space-related
technical subjects. NASA also sponsors or co-
authors publications, including articles in scientific and technical journals prepared by NASA personnel, textbooks and reference books sponsored by
NASA but published commercially, and AEC-NASA Tech
Briefs* and Technology Utilization Reports. Finally, NASA sponsors the publication, under NASA contract, of International Aerospace Abstracts (IAA)
by the American Institute of Aeronautics and Astronautics (AIAA) and various reliability abstracts
and technical reviews.[11]

NASA DISTRIBUTION POLICIES

Except for classified material or material
considered proprietary, the publications listed in
the preceding section are generally available to
all NASA-registered contractors free of charge, per
NASA distribution policy.[12] What has not been
widely discussed is the former NASA policy of only
limited distribution of Apollo technical reports.
This policy was discussed at a meeting with the
Director of TUD in December, 1967. No explanation
was offered; he noted only that NASA information
available to the RDC's for distribution contained
no Apollo information. This policy has since been
modified somewhat, but no information could be obtained on the policy shift.

Of course, contractor-supplied reports labeled
proprietary do not find their way into the RDC data
bank. No estimate can be made of the size of this
proprietary data bank because NASA TU personnel are
themselves either unaware of its size or do not
wish to discuss the matter. Two small technology-
based firms interviewed during the fieldwork felt

---

*AEC-NASA Tech Briefs are specially prepared
for TUD purposes, i.e., for commercial application.

that the information supplied by NERAC was unlikely
to contain any state-of-the-art materials, since
NASA contractors simply did not report advanced
technical work or, if they did, its distribution
was severely restricted. A number of Route 128
firms indicated the same feelings about what
government-sponsored technical information they
could obtain. Of course, the DOD information which
is supplied for inclusion in the STID collection
contains no classified or proprietary data. The
information is available free only through NASA
headquarters for prime contractors; subcontractors
must obtain the approval of their "primes."

NASA technical literature is also distributed
free of charge to other federal agencies, except
that material considered proprietary or restricted
is not generally made available. Tech Briefs are
mailed free of charge to over 11,000 individuals
and firms considered in some general way to be related to the space program; others may obtain a
subscription for $24 a year. NASA also distributes
non-limited and unclassified literature to fifty
public libraries located throughout the United
States and to eleven federal regional technical report centers, located primarily at major universities and other non-profit research centers. Complete magnetic tapes, including classified and
otherwise restricted materials, are made available
to eight NASA laboratories and sixteen large NASA
contractors. More limited versions of these tapes
are made available to the RDC's and to three "special users."[13]

In addition to this wide variety of technical
publication activities, NASA provides a number of
services designed to make aerospace technology more
generally available to commercial industry, other
government agencies, universities, and the public
at large. These services are under the functional,
and in most cases the direct, supervision of TUD.

Although the NASA TUP provides all the services listed below, most of the dissemination money

was spent on the nine RDC's and the computer dissemination program at the University of Georgia.[14]
With the closing of three centers--at the Midwest
Research Institute, Southeastern State College, and
Wayne State University--and the withdrawal of most
of the direct contract support for the RDC's at the
University of Indiana (1968) and the University of
Pittsburgh (1969), there may be some shift in TU
transfer emphasis. Very little information is yet
available as to whether these closings and the
slowing of funding do indicate a shift in TU transfer policy. However, much of the fiscal 1970 dissemination funds is still being spent on the remaining six RDC's and the computer program dissemination center.* These centers still represent the
most novel and the largest segment of the dissemination program.

Services of the NASA TUP[15]

    1. Operation (under contract) of nine RDC's
and a project for the analysis of the technology
dissemination program

    2. Information search and retrieval services
for industrial contractors

----

    *These closings may also reflect a need for
economies in view of the overall cutbacks in NASA
funding, so that TUD remains with about .01 percent
of NASA fiscal 1970 funding. 1970 NASA Authorization. Hearings, Pt. 1, pp. 1-2. In 1970 seven
technology application teams were formed at such
leading non-profit research centers as Stanford Research Institute, IIT Research Institute (Chicago),
and Research Triangle Institute (Durham, N.C.) to
investigate problems potentially amenable to solution by aerospace technology, but no funding figures are given for this effort. See Ronald Philips,
Director of TUD, Presentation to ICMA/NASA Working
Conference on Technology Transfer, October 21-23,
1970 (Washington, D.C.: NASA OTU).

3. A technological information utilization service, to identify technological advances having transfer potential and to respond to inquiries concerning them

4. Consultation with visitors to technology utilization field offices, and processing of telephone and mail inquiries for technical information at NASA field installations

5. The licensing of NASA-owned patents in cooperation with the office of the NASA Patent Counsel

6. Sponsorship of three biomedical application teams

7. Dissemination of computer programs developed by or for NASA

8. Distribution of selected British and Canadian documents, and documents of the Advisory Group for Aeronautical Research and Development

9. Cooperative programs with other agencies:

   a. Vocational Rehabilitation Administration

   b. Small Business Administration

   c. Office of Law Enforcement Assistance and the President's Commission on Law Enforcement and Administration of Justice

   d. Bureau of Public Roads

   e. Office of State Technical Services

   f. CFSTI.

The following additional services are being implemented:

10. Development of a NASA/SCAN information service to supplement the current SDI system for selective dissemination of information

11. Feasibility study of a computer-linked, direct-access, data retrieval system

12. Planned dissemination of NASA standard specifications data.

THE REGIONAL DISSEMINATION CENTERS

The delivery of tailored packages of knowledge in response to user needs is the aim of the experimental Regional Dissemination Centers established by NASA.[16]

This statement in the NASA TUP brochure states NASA's aim for the RDC's. The brochure also states that a broader aim is to educate industry to use externally generated knowledge through a "variety of services," including retrospective and current awareness literature searches.[17]

As of January 1, 1971, there were six operational centers and the center at the University of Georgia, which disseminates computer programs. All of these centers are located at universities, but there is some variation in organizational form and status at each university. The first list below shows the location of each RDC, and the second provides data on both NASA and industrial funds for all six operating RDC's.[18]

RDC Locations[19]

1. Aerospace Research Application Center*
    Indiana University
    Graduate School of Business

2. Aerospace Technology Research Applications**

---

*Now receiving only nominal support from NASA.

**Now closed.

Midwest Research Institute
Independent Regional Research Institute

3. Center for the Application of Science and
      Technology
    Wayne State University
    University Division of Urban Extension

4. Knowledge Availability Systems Center*
    University of Pittsburgh
    Computer and Information Sciences Center

5. Technology Application Center
    University of New Mexico
    University Bureau of Business Research

6. Southeastern State College (Okla.)**
    Separate Independent Collegiate Department

7. North Carolina Science and Technology
      Research Center
    State Board of Science and Technology

8. Western Research Application Center
    University of Southern California
    University Research Institute for Business
      and Economics

9. New England Research Application Center***
    University of Connecticut
    Graduate School of Business

---

*Now receiving only nominal support from NASA.

**Now closed.

***Threatened with contract termination unless substantial new industrial funds are solicited.

Funding for RDC's[20]

1. Aerospace Research Applications Center
    (Indiana University)

    NASA Funding (1963-68) $1,179,000*
    Industrial Income (1963-68)   795,000

    Number of companies paying annual member-
ship fees
            1963-----29   1966-----52
            1964-----34   1967-----71
            1965-----48   1968-----74

2. Knowledge Availability Systems Center
    (University of Pittsburgh)

    NASA Funding (1964-68) $1,049,000
    Industrial Income (1964-68)   341,000

    Number of companies paying annual member-
ship fees
            1964-----17   1967-----55
            1965-----47   1968-----40
            1966-----57

3. New England Research Application Center
    (University of Connecticut)

    NASA Funding (1966-68) $594,000
    Industrial Income (1966-68)   70,900
    Grant from Connecticut
      Research Commission   --

---

*This amount includes a $105,000 contract
which provides funding for three years, 1968-70.
This is an indication of progress toward self-
sufficiency, in that NASA support for the RDC
operation has now been reduced to $35,000 per year.

4. North Carolina Science and Technology
    Research Center

    NASA Funding (1964-68) $470,000
    Support by State of North Carolina   --
    Industrial Income (1966-68)   49,000

    Number of companies paying annual member-
ship fees
            1966------34   1968------31
            1967------31

    Number of additional companies served on
continuing fee basis that are not corporate
members of the RDC
            1966-------3   1968-------9
            1967-------8

5. Technology Application Center (University
    of New Mexico)

    NASA Funding (1964-68) $494,000
    University and State Funding   --
    Industrial Income   92,000

    Number of companies paying annual member-
ship fees
            1966------23   1968------27
            1967------17*

6. Western Research Application Center (Uni-
    versity of Southern California)

    NASA Funding (1966-68) $630,000
    Industrial Income (1967-68)   82,000

    All are established by means of a NASA con-
tract supervised by the TUD Director. Contracts
typically include the following terms and conditions:[21]

----

    *Plus five companies served on continuing fee
basis that are not corporate members of the RDC.

The RDC Director and all first-level supervision shall be approved by NASA.

All publications shall be cleared through NASA.

The RDC shall raise a stipulated amount of revenue, primarily from industrial firms.

Routinized feedback mechanisms shall be established.

NASA shall approve types of services to be provided and clients to be served.

Information about contract terms and conditions is based on an examination of contracts at three RDC's:

Midwest Research Institute, Wayne State University, and the University of Connecticut. Additional information was provided by a NASA memo discussing possible changes in contract provisions, most of which have now been incorporated in NASA RDC contracts.

In short, the contract between NASA and the university-based RDC is similar to that executed with any commercial industrial contractor and is unlike the more usual grant or contract used for university researchers. One major difference between an RDC and an industrial firm is the RDC's lack of bargaining power. Most of the RDC's have been established at less prestigious schools which have few alternative sources of income. Thus, the NASA TUD has largely been able to control RDC policy and even day-to-day operations, including the hiring and firing of RDC personnel.[22]

Contracts have varied in size from $100,000 to about $400,000, and the average has been about $250,000 yearly. Additional money has often been provided for special projects run by RDC personnel. The list below indicates some of these special projects.

Special Experimental Projects at RDC's[23]

Indiana University: University Consortium, Small Business Experiment, Management Information Service

Midwest Research Institute: Self-Supporting Seminars, Small Business Experiment, Capabilities Center Study

Wayne State University: Urban Studies, Small Business Experiment, Application of Aerospace Technology to Law Enforcement

University of Pittsburgh: Thesaural Development, Small Business Experiment

University of New Mexico: Natural Resources Services, Small Business Experiment

Southeastern State College: Mail/Telephone Marketing Experiment, Subject Seminars, Updating Regional Economic Studies.

The NASA TUD expects these centers to become self-supporting within five years or less, relying on fees from satisfied industrial clients.[24] The theory is that if these centers are offering valuable services to industrial firms, then these firms should be willing to pay fees covering the costs of the services. This requirement for self-support has had a number of consequences:

1. Three centers have been closed, and two others have had their scope substantially reduced.

2. The RDC's have concentrated on larger industrial clients as a means of obtaining maximum return for their sales efforts.

3. The centers have spent little or no time establishing effective feedback mechanisms, since fees (not feedback) are the key to continued NASA support.[25] TUD monitors two major items: (1)

document distribution statistics and (2) number of fee-paying industrial clients. Centers are generally required to undergo a review every six months. Several centers have recently been discontinued for failure to obtain sufficient fee-paying industrial clients, without regard to the long-term impact of these centers' activities or to the innovative approach to transfer taken by one of the centers.

Long-term employment contracts for center personnel have not been feasible because of year-to-year doubts about continued funding.

No real studies of the transfer process have been undertaken by any centers, since they were not felt likely to contribute to client fee solicitation.

NERAC AND ARAC: MAJOR SIMILARITIES AND DIFFERENCES OF TWO RDC'S

The industrial clients of NERAC and ARAC form the population covered in the fieldwork. NERAC is located at the University of Connecticut and is a department in the School of Business; ARAC is located at the University of Indiana and is a part of the Graduate School of Business, though its finances are handled through a legally separate non-profit corporation. Both centers were initiated and operated under fixed-price contracts from the NASA OTU. The operations of both centers are quite similar, in that they provide technical information searches for clients (mainly industrial) at a fee designed to cover out-of-pocket costs.

ARAC was the second RDC (established in January, 1963) and was considered a novel, experimental, user-oriented approach to transfer.[26] Following ARAC's initiation, eight other RDC's and the computer program dissemination center were established; this includes NERAC, which was established in March, 1967, after a nine-month market and feasibility study. Three of the eight have been closed for

failure to solicit sufficient industrial client
fees. ARAC itself has recently had most of its direct operating funding cut and now receives primarily special project money.[27] ARAC has, however,
become the most successful RDC in soliciting industrial fees, presently receiving about $180,000 an-
nually, which is about $100,000 short of its self-
sufficiency level. ARAC has also been the most
successful in terms of industrial clients under
yearly contract. These presently number about seventy, and another twenty are on a pay-as-you-go or
other special fee basis;[28] client renewals have
been running about 80 percent.[29]

NERAC, on the other hand, received less than
$20,000 from industrial clients during its first
full year of operation and appears likely to have
generated even less industrial client income during
its second year.* Additional funding was obtained
from the following sources: The Connecticut Research Commission ($15,000 for a project to provide
searches for Connecticut University researchers);
Connecticut STS Program ($15,000 for study of coat-
ing and joining of materials for Connecticut primary metals industry); NASA ($5,000 for assisting
Arthur D. Little NASA sponsored transfer study);
and University of Connecticut (about $5,000 for
searches for faculty). A total of about $40,000
for other non-industrial dissemination projects
has thus far been obtained. Costs of operation
have been estimated at $320,000/year including a
48 percent university overhead rate based on direct
labor costs. Its renewal or resubscription rate
has been running at less than 25 percent**

---

*Information obtained from NERAC/Cambridge of-
fice and interviews with NERAC personnel during
1968 and early 1969.

**This percentage figure is based on NERAC
client interviews. See Ch. 6, section entitled
"Implications of the Findings for the Hypotheses."

Presently, NERAC appears to have about ten yearly
clients and about six pay-as-you-go clients who
purchase an occasional search or two.* The NASA
OTU is quite concerned and has threatened to cut
off their funding several times if more industrial
fees were not obtained promptly. ARAC, on the
other hand, has become something of a paragon in
NASA's eyes as the only center that presently has
any prospects of becoming self-supporting.[30]

There are a number of differences in operations
and situs university support which may help to explain this difference in industrial support. Administrators at the University of Indiana vigorous-
ly supported ARAC from its inception, holding numerous meetings and making presentations to local
industry and alumni.** The University of Connecticut, on the other hand, gave NERAC little active
support other than providing physical facilities to
house the center's personnel and its computer.***
The university discouraged active solicitation of
alumni in local industry. Original corporate sub-
scriptions to ARAC amounted to over $50,000 during
its first year, exclusively from local industry,
industrial firms with alumni in management positions, or both.[31] However, this initial interested

---

*The acting NERAC Director was unwilling to
reveal an exact figure, but results of the fieldwork and interviews with other NERAC personnel indicate that these client figures are accurate.

**Data obtained from a series of interviews
with TUD personnel, a former TUD Director (who supervised several ARAC contracts), a former member
of the faculty at the Business School at Indiana,
and other RDC personnel, September, 1967-October,
1968.

***Conversations with the Dean of the Business
School at Connecticut, the NERAC Director, and other NERAC personnel, September, 1967-October, 1968.

support for ARAC does not account for its slow but
continued growth over the last five years. Some of
the factors which account for this continuing support appear to be the following:

ARAC initially solicited only yearly memberships of $3,000 or more, and thus clients had to
make a fairly substantial organizational commitment
for taking and at least reviewing ARAC-supplied materials.* Typically such a commitment would be hard
to rescind for a period of years, whether or not
the technology proved useful. Also, some member of
top management had probably himself become involved
in the review process, ensuring that company personnel would take some interest in the material as
it arrived.

Unlike the NERAC experience, most ARAC client
companies were exposed to a variety of searches, so
that one or even several poorly designed searches
would not cause the service to be dropped immediately.

ARAC worked exclusively with large companies,
where substantial expenditures for library resources
are common, and they worked through established information channels, thus ensuring a thorough understanding of ARAC information services by company
technical information personnel who in later years
would have to make the decision on whether or not
to retain ARAC services.

NERAC adopted a quite different initial marketing strategy. Without direct access to local corporate management under the auspices of its situs
university, it chose a direct, inexpensive trial as

---

*From field study interviews and personal in-
dustrial experience, it appears that decisions to
spend $3,000 or more must be made at least at the
vice-presidential or division general manager level
in most companies.

the selling method. Companies, large or small,
could try NERAC services for as little as $100 per
search, with no obligation to purchase any additional services. But NERAC has recently adopted a
quite different policy: selling primarily yearly
memberships for upwards of $1,000 per year, depend-
ing on the level of service desired.[32] (ARAC has
also recently adopted a policy of attempting to attract smaller clients by lowering its yearly membership rates.)

Another important difference is that ARAC has
always received the vigorous support of the NASA
TUP, often in the form of substantial grants for
additional projects, whereas NERAC was granted its
initial contract only reluctantly and has received
little additional NASA funding.*

Both centers are quite similar in the services
they offer, including retrospective and current
awareness technical literature searches. ARAC does
offer a number of packaged, standardized technical
information profiles in areas of general client interest, and recently NERAC has also tried to sell
standardized technical literature packages. Neither
center does any substantial amount of personal client counseling or inter-personal transfer. ARAC
states in its final report that such activities are

---

*ARAC received an extra $450,000 of funding in
1966. See Samuel Doctors, The Role of the Federal
Agencies in Technology Transfer (Cambridge, Mass.:
The MIT Press, 1969), Ch. 8, note 1. It has been
funded in other years for a variety of programs,
including a study of cost accounting for RDC's.
NERAC came into existence during one of the numerous changes in TU administration, and the new TUD
Director was reluctant to establish any new RDC's,
particularly near Boston, since the NASA Electronics
Research Center had just been established in Cambridge.

too expensive, given its need for self-support.*

Both centers employ more than twenty professionals, and their organizations include marketing,
computer operations, and literature searching functional areas. These centers also provide some opportunities for graduate students to participate in
center activities, mainly by assisting with computer operation in literature searching.

In sum, ARAC has thus far been the more successful in terms of obtaining industrial fees, but
it is still too early to tell how well NERAC will
do. Early prospects and lack of university support
would indicate a poor short-term prognosis for
NERAC's obtaining industrial fees. Neither center
does much more than selective document or abstract
dissemination, and neither does any research into
the transfer program.

---

*A letter from the ARAC Assistant Director in-
dicates that ARAC presently provides two basic services, retrospective and current awareness searches
of the literature. Letter from Robert Hull to
Samuel Doctors, February 24, 1969. This narrowing
of the service packages available was apparently to
cut back on expenses, in view of the withdrawal of
NASA operating funds in 1968.

NOTES

1.   See National Science Foundation, _Federal
Funds for Research, Development, and Other Scientific Activities: Fiscal Years 1968, 1969, and
1970_, NSF 69-31 (Washington, D.C.:   U.S. GPO, August, 1968), pp. vi-viii.

2.   See Samuel Doctors, _The Role of the Federal Agencies in Technology Transfer_ (Cambridge,
Mass.:   The MIT Press, 1969), Ch. 2, pp. 10-19, for
a detailed discussion of federal R&D spending patterns and policies.   See NSF, _op. cit._, and NSF,
Research and Development in Industry, 1967, NSF
69-28 (Washington, D.C.:   U.S. GPO, July, 1969).
Of the federal total, about 85 percent was spent in
two industries, aircraft/missiles and electronics/
communications, and by three federal agencies, AEC,
DOD, and NASA.   NSF 69-28, pp. 8-10; and Doctors,
loc cit.

3.   National Planning Association, "Technology
Transfer and Industrial Innovation," unpublished
report prepared for NSF by Sumner Myers, _et al_.
(Washington, D.C.:   NSF, February, 1967), pp. V-28
to V-32; Edward Roberts, "Entrepreneurship and
Technology," in Donald Marquis and William Gruber,
eds., _Factors in the Transfer of Technology_ (Cambridge, Mass.:   The MIT Press, 1969), p. 228.

4.   See Doctors, _op. cit._, Ch. 5, pp. 48-50,
for a detailed discussion of DOD transfer policies
and programs.   Also see Edward Furash, "The Problem of Technology Transfer," in Raymond Bauer and
Kenneth Gergen, eds., _The Study of Policy Formula-
tion_ (New York: The Free Press, 1968), pp. 289-300,
for a slightly different view of DOD transfer policies and programs.

5.   See Patent Provisions, Atomic Energy Act
of 1954, 42 U.S.C.A., secs. 2181-90, 2223.

6.   See Doctors, _op. cit._, Ch. 5, pp. 53-55,
and Appendix A, pp. 173-76, for an analysis of AEC

transfer programs and policies. See also Furash, op. cit., pp. 304-10.

7. For a general analysis of the NASA TUP, see Doctors, op. cit., Chs. 6-10. A somewhat different interpretation of the NASA TUP transfer activities is provided in Furash, op. cit., pp. 301-04; or see NASA, The Technology Utilization Program Review (Washington, D.C.: NASA OTU, February, 1967); and Useful New Technology from Aerospace Research and Development (Washington, D.C.: NASA OTU, 1970).

8. Some indication of the wide variety of transfer programs sponsored by the government is given in Doctors, op. cit., Ch. 5 and Appendix A.

9. A more complete description of STID functions and activities is provided in NASA, Technology Utilization Program Review (Washington, D.C.: NASA OTU, 1968). In fiscal 1968 STID was scheduled to receive over twice the direct appropriation of TUD, $11.7 million. U.S. Congress, House of Representatives, Committee on Science and Astronautics, Subcommittee on Advanced Research and Technology, 1968 NASA Authorization. Hearings, 90th Congress, first session (Washington, D.C.: U.S. GPO, 1967), Pt. 4, p. 714.

10. See U.S. Congress, House of Representatives, Committee on Science and Astronautics, Subcommittee on Advanced Research and Technology, 1970 NASA Authorization. Hearings, 91st Congress, first session (Washington, D.C.: U.S. GPO, 1969), Pt. 4, p. 701.

11. This compilation is taken from information supplied in DRI, Channels of Technology Acquisition in Commercial Firms and the NASA Dissemination Program (Springfield, Va.: CFSTI, June, 1967), p. 64. This report provides a description of each type of NASA publication, pp. 66-68.

12. The formal NASA distribution policies are listed in ibid., pp. 65-66.

13.   NASA, Technology Utilization Program; and Useful New Technology . . ., p. 12.   The tapes supplied to the RDC's and to special users (European Space Research Organization, Chemical Propulsion Information Agency, and CFSTI) contain no classified or limited distribution material.

14.   See Doctors, op. cit., Ch. 8, note 1, estimating that 90 percent of fiscal 1967 revenues for dissemination were spent on RDC operations. See also 1970 NASA Authorization. Hearings, pp. 700-21.

15.   DRI, op. cit., p. 70; and 1970 NASA Authorization. Hearings, Pt. 4, pp. 700-23.

16.   NASA, Technology Utilization Program, p. 21.

17.   Ibid., p. 22.

18.   See Doctors, op. cit., Ch. 8, for a detailed analysis of RDC organizational status and the effects of different situs university policies on RDC operations, including funding.

19.   NASA, Technology Utilization Program, p. 38; and U.S. Congress, House of Representatives, Committee on Science and Astronautics, Subcommittee on Advanced Research and Technology, 1970 NASA Authorization. Hearings, 91st Congress, final session (Washington, D.C.: U.S. GPO, 1970), Pt. 4, pp. 700-22.

20.   1970 NASA Authorization. Hearings, 91st Congress, final session, p. 721.   RDC industrial funding increased 18 percent between calendar year 1969 and 1970 to a total annual level of $520,000 in 1970.   (Information supplied by NASA, April 7, 1971.)

21.   See NASA, "Memorandum Concerning Selected Provisions for Inclusions in Technology Utilization Division Contracts as Appropriate" (Washington, D.C.: NASA OTU, October 15, 1967).   Information

about contract terms and administration was also
obtained from numerous interviews with RDC and OTU
personnel, 1966-68.

22. See Doctors, op. cit., Ch. 9, for a detailed analysis of RDC contract administration and
its effects on RDC operation and morale.

23. NASA, Technology Utilization Program,
p. 38.

24. Ibid., p. 22; and any NASA authorization
hearing, 1963 to the present.

25. See NERAC, An Account of the Activities
and Results of the First Year of Operation of the
New England Research Application Center, prepared
under Contract NSR 07-002-029 (Storrs, Conn.:
NERAC, March 31, 1968), pp. 26-27, indicating that
this RDC does not feel it can afford to worry about
establishing feedback mechanisms or studying the
transfer process, given TUP pressure to obtain industrial fees.

26. See, for example, the discussion in
Furash, op. cit., pp. 303-04.

27. ARAC, Final Five-Year Report, Experiment
to Transfer Technology from a University-Based
Center, NASA Contract SC-NASA-162 (Bloomington,
Ind.: ARAC, February, 1968), pp. 31-32.

28. Ibid., p. 22; and list of RDC client companies supplied by the NASA TUP. However, the
twenty-three questionnaires returned in this study
indicate that the official ARAC renewal rates may
be overly optimistic.

29. Ibid.

30. ARAC's industrial client support was the
only extensive discussion of RDC industrial support
listed as part of 1968 NASA Authorization. Hearings, pp. 673-737, esp. pp. 677-79. See also NASA,
Technology Utilization Program, pp. 22-25.

31.   ARAC, op. cit., pp. 19-21, lists twenty-nine original clients, almost all of whom were located in Indiana and a few in immediately adjacent states.   More important, all of these original companies attended presentations by Arthur Weimer and other University of Indiana administrators to encourage them to support ARAC.

32.   See Doctors, op. cit., Ch. 6, p. 128. Satisfaction and renewal appear to be highly correlated with repeated use, and a number of NERAC clients who expressed dissatisfaction with NERAC-supplied information indicated that the one or two trial searches had not been well structured for their problem or had produced very little useful material.

5

METHODOLOGY
OF THE
STUDY

STUDY DESIGN

The study design used to examine the hypotheses given in Chapter 1 made use of in-depth personal interviews with RDC industrial clients and questionnaires of two types: the RDC (NERAC or ARAC) Client Questionnaire (CQ), which was used mainly as a guide for personal interviews, and the Selected Corporate Technologist Questionnaire (SCTQ), which was filled out by each company user of RDC services that could be identified during the interview sessions. (Copies of both questionnaires are included in Appendix B.) The RDC CQ was also used for obtaining data from ARAC industrial clients and from the four NERAC clients who declined to participate in on-site interviews. Thus, some uniformity was obtained in the data collection.

In addition, the fieldwork results were compared with other studies of the effectiveness of the NASA dissemination program and with studies of other methods of horizontal transfer. The primary focus of the fieldwork was a series of in-depth personal interviews with forty-eight of the fifty-four industrial clients of NERAC, the RDC serving

the New England region. The on-site personal interviews were supplemented with mail questionnaires
sent to sixty ARAC industrial clients.

FIELDWORK

The fieldwork was designed to determine the
effectiveness of the NASA RDC system of technology
transfer. Personal interviews with management and
other users of RDC services was the primary mode of
data collection. These interviews were conducted
at the company or corporate division which had con-
tracted for NERAC's services.

The field study was conducted over a period of
three months, beginning in November, 1968, and end-
ing early in February, 1969. Fifty-four companies
were contacted by a form letter which described the
nature of the transfer problem in this country, the
focus of the field study, and the reason for seek-
ing an interview. The establishment, whether a
company or a division of a larger corporate unit,
was used as the organizational unit to be considered in determining transfer or in examining the
hypotheses. However, when the establishment was
the corporation's central R&D group (Polaroid) or
staff group (Raytheon), the corporation was considered the unit of analysis.

Within a few weeks after the letter was sent,
each company was contacted by telephone to arrange
a time for an on-site interview. The list of NERAC
client companies was compiled from the files of the
NERAC Cambridge office and checked against a list
supplied by the NASA TUP. The NASA list included
only ten yearly clients and six pay-as-you-go clients, while the list obtained directly from NERAC
included fifty-nine client companies, undifferen-
tiated as to the terms of their respective contracts. Apparently there is some lag in NERAC's
reporting to the TUP office. The NASA list was
complete as of July 1, 1968, as was the NERAC list.
However, five companies included on the NERAC

supplied list proved to have been included errone-
ously.

Of the fifty-four companies contacted, two
could not be located in standard industrial or
state directories, four declined to participate in
the study, and four declined to participate in on-
site interviews but expressed willingness to discuss their experiences with NERAC over the telephone and to complete both questionnaires. The remaining forty-four companies or corporate divisions
were interviewed on-site about their NASA RDC experience, using the NERAC CQ as a guide for data collection. Each identifiable technical user of RDC-
supplied technology was also requested to complete
an SCTQ. Not all users of NERAC-supplied technology could be found at interview time, a few being
out of town or having left the employ of the company, but over 80 percent of all NERAC technology
users in the forty-four companies did participate
in this field study; a similar percentage holds for
those companies interviewed by phone (a total of
sixty users, mainly engineers or scientists).

In addition to the interviews conducted with
NERAC RDC clients, mail questionnaires were sent to
sixty industrial clients of ARAC. This secondary
source of data was used as a general check on the
primary source, to minimize the bias in the primary
sample due to the shorter time duration of the
NERAC program, and to examine the RDC program in a
different geographical and industrial setting.
ARAC was established in 1963, and is the second
oldest RDC program.

The sixty ARAC client companies were contacted
by means of a form letter somewhat different from
that used to contact NERAC clients. One copy of
the RDC CQ was included with this form letter as
were three copies of the SCTQ. The companies were
requested to have someone familiar with overall new
technology planning complete the former and persons
actually using ARAC-supplied technology complete
the latter questionnaires. Twenty-three client

companies completed the questionnaires; one company supplied useful data; another six indicated that they found so little use for the technology that they did not feel qualified to respond; and two claimed never to have purchased any RDC services. Thus, slightly over 38 percent of those companies contacted returned completed questionnaires. Several companies originally declined to complete questionnaires, but did so upon a subsequent request indicating that I wished as comprehensive a sample as possible, even if their experiences were negative.

Thus, overall, 89 percent of NERAC client firms participated in the fieldwork, whereas 50 percent of ARAC firms contacted only by mail responded and 40 percent participated actively. The difference in response between NERAC and ARAC clients may be partially explained by several factors:

1. Some of the questions, particularly those concerning new product planning, division-level sales, R&D spending, and growth rates, are considered company proprietary information and may be discussed to some extent in person but will not be written down, as a matter of company policy.

2. General reluctance to complete relatively lengthy questionnaires. Only one of four NERAC clients contacted solely by mail even responded.

3. Time itself may have been a factor, since an average of only four weeks was allowed for return of the ARAC questionnaires.*

---

*The ARAC client letters were sent in several batches, approximately between January 17, 1969, and February 18, 1969. The cutoff date for accepting returns for the study was March 20, 1969. Four of the companies on the ARAC sample indicated that they had never been ARAC clients.

Because of the better and more complete data
to be expected from personal interviews and because
of the complexity of the transfer process, this
study has placed primary reliance on the personal
interviews, which allowed a variety of questions
(depending on response and context) and flexibility
of approach not possible in a mail questionnaire.
The written questionnaires provided some check on
interview bias. The rationale for directing the
major portion of the field study at NERAC industrial clients is as follows:

1. Some direct comparison with Edward Roberts'
Boston Route 128 spin-off company sample was possible, since three of the companies were common to
both studies; more important, ten other companies
in the present sample were similar in their technical sophistication and interest in the space/defense
market and about of the same size as those in the
MIT spin-off sample. Thus, some overall comparison
of transfer method effectiveness was possible.[1]

2. Personal acquaintance with some of the
company managers and technologists allowed more direct access to sensitive data and more candor during the interview sessions. Further, prior interviews conducted with many of these same conducted
with many of these same companies provided some
background data for comparison and validation of
data collected from the fieldwork.*

3. Detailed data on NERAC client contacts,
operations, policies, and problems was readily
available. The effect of NASA TUP policies and

---

*It is hoped that some acquaintance with a
number of the NERAC clients did not result in any
bias during the interview sessions. On a number of
occasions it did provide more candor during the
interview sessions and did ease the problem of obtaining on-site interviews. Fourteen of the NERAC
clients had previously been contacted by me.

technical supervision upon center activities could
be more easily observed.

SCOPE OF THE FIELDWORK

The primary focus of the study was on the
transfer of specific items of aerospace technology
for commercial application. However, a number of
the small and medium-size firms operate in both
the commercial and the aerospace markets, and it
was difficult to isolate exact applications of the
technology. Also, it was in many cases difficult
to trace the application of specific items of technology, since it appears that these specific items
were only part of the complex process of transfer.
In addition, some firms were reluctant to discuss
specific usage, especially where a new product idea
was involved. For these reasons, the study also
considered more general types of transfer, as when
RDC-supplied technology provided state-of-the-art
information for new product planning or when it was
used as background for technical problem solving.

The study also examined the RDC role in general, as an external technology transfer agent, since
much of the RDC effort is now directed to supplying
more general, non-space/defense technology. All
the satisfied commercial clients of NERAC received
primarily non-space/defense technology. Thus, as
part of the study, some consideration was given to
this new aspect of RDC operation, one not originally contemplated by NASA. The RDC as a more general
transfer agent may, in fact, tend to create a
greater receptivity for externally generated technology.[2]

Besides examples of specific item or more general area transfer, client satisfaction and willingness to renew their contracts with the RDC were
used as some indication of potential usefulness of
NERAC services and perhaps of longer-term transfer
possibilities. Although the willingness of RDC
clients to renew their contracts is some indication

of usefulness of RDC-supplied technology, it is not
conclusive, since a variety of other motivations
may be operative.

DATA ANALYSIS METHODOLOGY

Both the in-depth personal interviews and the
mail questionnaires attempted to obtain data in
five general areas:

1. Technology transfer that had occurred using RDC-supplied technology

2. Other sources of space/defense technology
adapted for commercial application

3. Usage profile, which included what kinds
of information were received, who used the information, for what purposes it was used, and how satisfied the recipients were with this information

4. Client company characteristics which
seemed to be related to the acceptance of externally generated technology, particularly space/defense
technology

5. Individual technologist (or other user)
usage of RDC and other sources of space/defense
technology and his perception of their value to
him, both individually and comparatively.

Two methods of gathering data were used during
the interviews. First, a question-and-answer session was held with company personnel concerned with
NERAC-supplied technology, using the CQ as a guide;
then each user was requested to complete a SCTQ, as
a check on bias during the personal interview and
also to give each user an opportunity to express
his perceptions and use of NERAC supplied technology directly, without the interview acting as an
intermediary.

A total of almost ninety client company employees were interviewed, including top management,

functional managers, and professionals (engineers, scientists, and information specialists). Of the ninety, only sixty claimed to have actively used the NERAC-supplied information; the other thirty supplied some general information about the company, about technical information resources commonly employed, and about transfer planned or completed. The participants were asked to indicate what types of technology were supplied by NERAC, whether space/defense or purely open literature or both.* They were also asked to indicate whether any inter-personal services, such as consulting and counseling, were supplied, in order to see whether transfer and inter-personal contact might be related. Also, the participants were asked to indicate whether narrow, problem-oriented information or more general background information was supplied.

The participants were asked to indicate their organizational affiliation and their uses(s) of the information, whether for planning, technical problem solving, survey of competition, or other(s). This area of response was also checked on the SCTQ to determine whether their perception and use of RDC technology was the same as or different from their answers during the question-and-answer session. Participants were asked, both in the

_____

*Open literature is defined to include the scientific-peer reference literature, such as <u>Physical Review</u> and <u>Annals of Mathematics</u>, as well as the technical trade press, such as <u>Industrial Research</u> and <u>Electronics World</u>. This literature, of course, contains some research results sponsored by space/defense R&D, but it also contains, depending on the publication, a large portion of non-space/defense-oriented R&D results. When used in this study, the term "open literature" will refer primarily to publications containing either the results of pure research or to those containing non-space/defense-applied research and developments, such as <u>Chemistry and Industry</u> and <u>Research/Development</u>.

question-and-answer session and on the SCTQ, to de-
scribe any transfers that had occurred from RDC-
supplied technology and/or from other sources of
space/defense technology. Some check on this area
was provided by studies done by NERAC and ARAC on
client usage and transfer.[3]

The fact that industrial clients were willing
to purchase RDC information and expend personnel
time to review this information was felt to be some
indication of the information's usefulness where
transfer could not otherwise be identified. However, this criterion of usefulness was also checked
by discussing company satisfaction with RDC technology, and by asking each user to indicate whether
or not he felt it had been of some specific use and
how he would rate this source of technical information as compared with others he commonly employed
(both space/defense and non-space/defense). As a
measure both of transfer and of usefulness, each
user was asked to place a monetary value on NERAC
services and to compare this value with the cost.

Renewal or failure to renew was felt to be an
indirect measure of transfer and a direct measure
of perceived usefulness. Therefore, interviewees
were encouraged to discuss their plan for renewal
or reasons against such renewal. Interviewees were
also asked to discuss their specific ideas about
the usefulness of space/defense technology on both
a short-term and a long-term basis, regardless of
their action on renewal.

It was hoped that there would be some correla-
tion between company receptivity and externally
generated space/defense technology and the following:

1. Technical sophistication of product line

2. A high ratio of R&D spending to sales and
a high ratio of technologists to total employment

3. The operation of a separate R&D facility,
not functionally part of an operating division

4. Sales in the space/defense market.

It was also hoped that any bias to present only favorable comments about the usefulness of RDC-supplied information would be minimized by the number of related questions in different contexts addressed to this issue on both questionnaires.

NOTES

1. See Ch. 6, section entitled "Characteristics of the Sample," for a definition of Boston Route 128 spin-off company characteristics. Fifty percent of the NERAC sample were in electronics, electronic component material development, or instrumentation. See Table 7. For a description of the MIT spin-off sample, see Edward Roberts, "Entrepreneurship and Technology," in Factors in the Transfer of Technology, Donald Marquis and William Gruber, eds. (Cambridge, Mass.: The MIT Press, 1969), pp. 219-37.

2. See Samuel Doctors, The Role of the Federal Agencies in Technology Transfer (Cambridge, Mass.: The MIT Press, 1969), Ch. 8, pp. 101-05, for a detailed analysis of this measure of RDC effectiveness. However, in the case of NERAC it may be a more reliable indication of usefulness to the client, since no university pressure was brought to bear on alumni or local industry. NERAC sold its services in the open market.

3. The results of these studies are discussed in Ch. 2, section entitled "ARAC/NERAC Studies."

6

FIELDWORK
RESULTS
AND
INTERPRETATION

This chapter presents the results of the fieldwork and an interpretation of those results in
light of the hypotheses advanced in Chapter 3. The
chapter is divided into four sections: (1) presentation of the general findings of the fieldwork;
(2) description and analysis of examples of specific
item transfer or potential transfer; (3) discussion
of the findings as they relate to the hypotheses;
(4) presentation of the conclusions, implications
for future study, and limitations of the fieldwork.

GENERAL FIELDWORK RESULTS

Characteristics of the Sample

The primary fieldwork sample was formed from
fifty-four NERAC clients, both past and present.
Some of these clients have purchased yearly service contracts, but most have purchased services
only as needed. Forty of the companies are located in Massachusetts, most of them (twenty-seven)
in the Greater Boston area; twelve of the remaining

fourteen are located in Connecticut, one in Vermont, and one in New York.*

The forty-eight companies which participated in the fieldwork are reasonably representative of technically based New England manufacturers and are distributed within the various industrial groupings as shown in Table 7.

The NERAC clients as individual companies were well above the national average of a 2.7 percent ratio of technologists to total employment (in 1967). (See Tables 8 and 9.) More than 65 percent of the firms had a ratio of technologists to total employment greater than this 2.7 percent; 40 percent had a ratio of 10 percent or higher.** As might be

----

*The ARAC sample, twenty-three responding firms, were located primarily in the Midwest (twenty-one of twenty-three); eleven in Indiana, five in Ohio, five in Illinois, and one each in Oklahoma and Pennsylvania.

**The national average figure was computed by dividing the total employment figures of responding firms by the total number of R&D scientists and engineers. NSF, Research and Development in Industry, 1967, NSF 69-28 (Washington, D.C.: U.S. GPO, July, 1969), p. 51. The NSF table showing the number of R&D technologists per 1,000 employees is reproduced as Table 9 and may be compared with Table 7 on an industry-by-industry basis. (Engineering figures are for 1968.) Although much of the data is presented in joint NERAC/ARAC tables, the data obtained from ARAC clients were clearly not as complete or as thoroughly cross-checked as that obtained from NERAC clients, since it came solely from mail questionnaires. Thus, it is intended only to provide some additional background data for the primary sample results.

expected from these results, a large number of the
firms (48 percent) had a ratio of R&D performance
to total sales greater than the national average of
4.2 percent (in 1967).*   (See Tables 10 and 11.)
Another characteristic of the NERAC sample firms
was their high percentage of sales to the federal
government, primarily in the space/defense market.**

---

*The apparent inconsistency between the
technologists-to-employment ratio and the R&D
performance-to-sales ratio is explained by the fact
that small companies spend much less per R&D technologist than larger companies. Almost 70 percent
of the NERAC companies had less than 1,000 employees.
NSF figures indicate an average of $42,800 for all
R&D-performing companies and an average of $24,400
for R&D-performing companies with less than 1,000
employees; $34,400 for companies with 1,000-4,999
employees; and $45,700 for companies with over
5,000 employees. Of particular relevance for the
NERAC sample are the figures for electrical equipment and communications.

Total Employment (1968 figures)

Average	Under 1,000	1,000 to 4,999	5,000 to 9,999	10,000 or more
$39,100	$20,200	$36,200	$36,000	$40,400

Source: NSF, Research and Development in Industry,
1967 (Washington, D.C.: U.S. GPO, July, 1969), p. 53.

**During the forty-eight interviews, indirect
as well as direct sales to the government were explored. The figures presented in Tables 12 and 13
represent, insofar as data were available, a composite figure. However, it is not entirely clear
from the ARAC client responses that they inter-
preted Question 11 on the CQ to include indirect
as well as direct sales to government prime contractors or subcontractors where end use is for a
space/defense project.

TABLE 7

Industrial Distribution of NERAC Sample

SIC Code[a]	Industrial Group	Number of Companies	Percent of Sample	Industrial Group as a Percent of Total New England Manufacturing Employment
28	Chemicals and allied products	5	10.4	2.2
33	Primary metals	1	2.1	4.3
34	Fabricated metal products (includes valves and other mechanical control devices)	6	12.5	6.6
35	Machinery, machine tools, and components	8	16.7	11.0
36, 38[b]	Electronics and instrumentation	20	52.0	15.0
	Non-metallic materials (mainly for electrical components)	5̲ 25		
39	Miscellaneous	3	6.3	4.8

The SIC Code is the Standard Industrial Classification Code, whereby industries are arrayed for statistical tables in terms of specific industries, industry groups, and product fields. For further information, see NSF, Research and Development in Industry, 1967, NSF 69-28 (Washington, D.C.: U.S. GPO, July, 1969), Appendix A; or Bureau of the Budget, Standard Industrial Classification Manual (Washington, D.C.: U.S. GPO, 1967). Standard Industrial Classification groupings can be quite misleading, since companies making cleaning compounds are grouped with drug and chemical companies; and more disparate conglomerates are grouped under one category although their independent divisions engage in numerous businesses. Thus SIC or other standard industrial groupings are used sparingly in this study.

[b]There were only two companies that could be grouped in the instrumentation area, but their interests were closely allied to electrical equipment and components and so have been functionally grouped with the electronic establishments. The non-metallic material manufacturers could have been placed in several other groups, but because their primary end use is electronic components and because their technical interests were similar to other electronic establishments, they have also been placed in the electronics grouping.

Sources: Author's data analysis; U.S. Department of Commerce, County Business Patterns, 1965 (Washington, D.C.: U.S. GPO, 1967).

111

TABLE 8

Ratio of R&D Technologists to Total Employment,
NERAC and ARAC Samples

Sample	Number of Firms	Percent of Sample	Ratio of Technologists to Employment (percent)
NERAC	17	35.4	0 - 3
	12	25.0	4 - 9
	10	21.0	10 - 15
	9	18.7	Over 15
ARAC	17	74.0	0 - 3
	3	13.0	4 - 9
	1	4.4	10 - 15
	2	8.7	Over 15

Source: Author's data analysis.

Almost 50 percent of the NERAC clients sold 20 percent or more of their total sales volume to the government; 21 percent performed substantial amounts
of R&D for the government (more than 10 percent of
their sales represented by R&D sales to federal
agencies). (See Tables 12 and 13.)

The sample was also distinguished by the small
size of the companies, as measured by either annual
sales or total employment. Fifty-six percent of the
firms had sales between $10 million and $100 million.
Almost 69 percent of the firms had less than 1,000
employees. (See Tables 14 and 15.)

The firms were also characterized by a generally high sales growth rate; 66 percent had experienced an average growth rate greater than 6 percent
over the last three years, and 38 percent had averaged better than 11 percent per year.* The thirteen
spin-off-type firms had an average growth rate of
better than 20 percent (compounded) over the past
three years. The eight machine tool companies, on
the other hand, had averaged less than 2 percent
per year. (See Table 16.)

A Route 128-type spin-off is defined for this
study as a technically based firm with sales under
$10 million in 1970 which was founded primarily by
men with a technical and/or scientific background;
was established within the last fifteen years to
sell services and products primarily in the space/
defense market; has experienced a period of very
rapid growth; and has diversified substantially
into commercial markets during this rapid growth
period.[1]

---

*I would have liked to gather more data on
profit growth rates as well as sales, but a number
of companies were quite reluctant to discuss their
profit figures. However, most of those firms with
the higher growth rates indicated that their
profits had kept pace with their sales.

TABLE 9

Full-Time-Equivalent Number of R&D Scientists and Engineers per
1,000 Employees, by Industry and Size of Company, 1958-67

Industry and Size of Company	SIC Code
Total	
Distribution by Industry	
Food and kindred products	20
Textiles and apparel	22,23
Lumber, wood products, and furniture	24,25
Paper and allied products	26
Chemicals and allied products	28
Industrial chemicals	281-82
Drugs and medicines	283
Other chemicals	284-87,289
Petroleum refining and extraction	29,13
Rubber products	30
Stone, clay, and glass products	32
Primary metals	33
Ferrous metals and products[a]	331-32,3391,3399[c]
Non-ferrous metals and products	balance of 33
Fabricated metal products	34
Machinery	35
Electrical equipment and communication	36,48
Radio and TV receiving equipment	365
Communication equipment and electronic components	366-67,48
Other electrical equipment	361-64,369
Motor vehicles and other transportation equipment	371,373-75,379
Aircraft and missiles	372,19
Professional and scientific instruments	38
Scientific and mechanical measuring instruments	381-82
Optical, surgical, photographic, and other instruments	383-87
Other manufacturing industries	21,27,31,39)
Non-manufacturing industries	10-12,14-17,)
	40-47,49-67,)
	70-79,89)

Distribution by Size of Company
  (based on number of employees)
Less than 1,000
1,000 to 4,999
5,000 to 9,999
10,000 or more

Note: The full-time-equivalent number of R&D scientists and engineers per 1,000 employees in 1966 was derived by dividing the arithmetic mean of the full-time-equivalent number of R&D scientists and engineers employed in mid-January, 1966, and mid-January, 1967, by the number of company employees in all activities (in thousands), in March, 1966. Similar procedures were used to compute ratios for 1958-65. For 1967 data were derived by dividing man-years of R&D scientists and engineers for 1967 by March, 1967, employment figures.

1958	1959	1960	1961	1962	1963	1964	1965	1966	1967
21	24	25	28	28	28	30	30	27	27
6	7	7	6	7	7	7	7	7	7
1	2	2	3	a	3	3	3	3	3
5	8	7	4	6	4	5	5	4	4
6	6	6	6	6	6	6	6	6	6
39	40	46	40	38	40	41	39	38	36
42	42	46	43	38	40	40	38	35	33
46	42	50	42	44	47	54	53	53	51
30	34	41	32	33	38	33	32	35	33
15	14	18	19	18	17	16	17	17	18
19	18	19	20	20	20	19	18	17	17
a	b	b	12	12	12	12	12	13	14
5	5	6	7	6	5	5	5	5	5
4	4	4	5	4	4	4	4	4	4
6	7	10	11	11	8	8	8	8	8
16	17	13	17	16	15	16	15	13	14
24	24	28	28	26	28	28	27	27	28
43	42	51	54	54	55	55	53	44	43
d	d	d	d	d	d	d	d	d	18
52	47	62	66	67	67	69	66	53	52
37	38	41	42	1	41	40	39	38	35
16	16	14	20	20	19	20	20	20	20
72	73	85	91	87	99	110	113	95	89
44	47	31	39	36	36	37	36	33	32
57	64	46	45	43	38	35	33	28	26
33	34	23	34	31	35	38	39	36	35
			(9	8	9	8	8	7	6
a	10	8	(8	8	9	11	10	12	13
			(						
			(						
18	24	23	26	27	27	27	27	28	28
12	14	16	18	19	19	19	18	16	16
)25	20	28	30	30	31	32	31	30	(15
)									(31

a Not available separately but included in total.
b Data included in the other manufacturing industries group.
c SIC codes 3391 and 3399 included in the non-ferrous metals and products group for 1958-66.
d Included in the other electrical equipment group.

Source: NSF, Research and Development in Industry, 1967, NSF 69-28 (Washington, D.C.: U.S. GPO, July, 1969), p. 51.

TABLE 10

Ratio of R&D Performance to Sales,
NERAC and ARAC Samples

Sample	Number of Firms	Percent of Sample	R&D as Percent of Sales
NERAC	18	37.6	0 - 2
	7	14.8	3 - 5
	9	18.8	6 - 10
	5	10.4	11 - 15
	9	18.8	Over 15
ARAC	13	56.5	0 - 2
	4	17.4	3 - 5
	4	17.4	6 - 10
	0	----	11 - 15
	2	8.7	Over 15

Source: Author's data analysis.

The ARAC sample of twenty-three companies had
quite a different composition. Few of the firms
exhibited a highly sophisticated technical base.
Over half of the sample firms were in more mature
industries, such as automobile components (21.7 percent) and machine tools or components (13 percent);
the other five firms (22 percent) were in furniture,
petroleum, rubber, and glass. (See Table 17.)
Seventy-four percent of the ARAC firms had a ratio
of R&D technologists to total employment between 0
and 3 percent, and only two firms (both space/
defense contractors) had a ratio above 11 percent.
Similarly, the average ARAC client ratio of R&D performance to sales was much lower than that of the
average NERAC client. The companies sold very
little, on the average, to the government; 87 percent sold 10 percent or less of their products to
the government, and only two of the firms sold any
R&D to the government.*

Not only was the ARAC group different in its
technical base, but the companies were on the average much larger than the NERAC clients. Eighty percent had over 1,000 employees and had annual sales
in excess of $10 million. It was quite difficult
to compare the two samples in terms of growth rates,
since only 65 percent of the ARAC sample answered
the question concerning growth rate. However, for
the data given, the ARAC clients were quite high in
average growth rate, with over 50 percent experiencing an average rate of 11 percent or more.

————————————

*Apparently ARAC clients do not use as many
non-RDC sources of space/defense technology as do
NERAC clients. Sixty percent of NERAC clients use
other sources of space/defense technology, while
only 44 percent of ARAC clients do.

TABLE 11

Funds for R&D Performance as Percent of Net Sales in R&D-Performing
Manufacturing Companies, by Industry and Size of Company, 1957-67

Industry and Size of Company	SIC Code
Total	
Distribution by Industry	
Food and kindred products	20
Textiles and apparel	22,23
Lumber, wood products, and furniture	24,25
Paper and allied products	26
Chemicals and allied products	28
Industrial chemicals	281-82
Drugs and medicines	283
Other chemicals	284-89
Petroleum refining and extraction	29,13
Rubber products	30
Stone, clay, and glass products	32
Primary metals	33
Ferrous metals and products[c]	331-32,3391,3399
Non-ferrous metals and products	balance of 33
Fabricated metal products	34
Machinery	35
Electrical and communication equipment	36,48
Radio and TV receiving equipment	365
Communication equipment and electronic components	366-67,48
Other electrical equipment	361-64,369
Motor vehicles and other transportation equipment	361,373-79
Aircraft and missiles	372,19
Professional and scientific instruments	38
Scientific and mechanical measuring instruments	381-82
Optical, surgical, photographic, and other instruments	383-87
Other manufacturing industries	21,27,31,39
Distribution by Size of Company	
(based on number of employees)	
Less than 1,000	
1,000 to 4,999	
5,000 to 9,999	
10,000 or more	

[a]Not available separately but included in total.

[b]Included in the other manufacturing industries group.

[c]SIC codes 3391 and 3399 are included in the non-ferrous metals
and products group, 1957-65.

[d]Included in the other electrical equipment group.

1957	1958	1959	1960	1961	1962	1963	1964	1965	1966	1967
3.4	3.8	3.9	4.2	4.3	4.3	4.5	4.6	4.3	4.2	4.2
.3	.3	.3	.4	.4	.4	.4	.4	.4	.4	.4
a	.3	.5	.6	.5	.4	.5	.5	.5	.5	.5
a	.4	.5	.6	.5	.5	.5	.5	.4	.4	.4
.6	.7	.6	.7	.7	.7	.8	.7	.7	.7	.7
3.5	3.8	3.9	4.5	4.3	4.2	4.3	4.5	4.2	4.2	4.3
5.0	5.4	4.8	5.7	5.2	4.9	5.1	5.0	4.6	4.5	4.5
3.6	4.1	4.2	4.6	4.3	4.3	4.7	5.9	5.7	6.2	6.1
1.3	1.5	2.0	2.2	2.8	3.0	2.8	2.5	2.3	2.3	2.4
.7	1.1	1.0	1.0	1.0	1.0	1.0	1.2	1.1	1.0	1.0
1.7	1.8	2.0	2.0	2.2	2.1	2.3	2.1	2.0	2.0	2.1
b	b	b	1.6	1.5	1.6	1.6	1.6	1.6	1.6	1.9
.5	.7	.6	.8	.8	.8	.8	.8	.8	.7	.8
a	.6	.5	.6	.7	.6	.7	.7	.7	.7	.7
a	.7	.9	1.0	1.2	1.1	1.1	1.0	.9	.8	1.0
1.6	1.7	1.4	1.3	1.4	1.5	1.6	1.5	1.3	1.3	1.3
3.4	3.8	4.3	4.7	4.2	4.0	4.2	4.3	4.1	3.9	4.3
7.6	10.3	11.0	11.2	10.1	9.9	10.1	9.8	9.5	8.6	8.5
d	d	d	d	d	d	d	d	d	2.4	2.9
a	11.3	12.6	13.1	12.7	12.8	13.0	13.0	12.3	10.4	10.1
a	9.7	9.4	9.1	8.0	7.3	7.3	7.0	7.1	7.4	7.5
2.9	4.2	2.9	3.0	4.0	3.5	3.4	3.6	3.1	3.2	3.4
16.8	17.7	20.7	23.2	23.5	23.8	26.7	28.9	28.1	25.3	21.5
7.0	7.8	7.2	6.3	6.0	6.3	5.9	6.1	6.1	5.6	5.4
9.5	10.2	9.7	8.6	6.0	5.4	4.1	4.2	3.8	3.3	3.1
5.2	6.3	5.8	5.3	6.1	6.8	6.9	7.0	7.1	6.5	6.3
a	1.3	.7	.4	.4	.7	.7	.7	.7	.6	.6
1.8	1.3	1.7	1.6	1.8	1,8	1.9	2.4	2.1	2.7	2.9
1.8[e]	1.8	1.8	2.2	2.2	2.2	2.4	1.8	2.0	2.3	2.3
)3.9[e]	4.8	4.8	5.1	5.2	5.0	5.3	5.3	4.6	(1.9	2.0
)									(5.3	5.2

[e]Separate data for companies with 5,000 or more employees
and for companies with 1,000 to 4,999 employees were estimated
for 1957 by NSF. Revisions of R&D statistics by the U.S. Bureau
of the Census for this year did not yield separate data for companies in these size groups.

Source: NSF, Research and Development in Industry, 1967, NSF 69-28 (Washington, D.C.: U.S. GPO, July, 1969), p. 58.

TABLE 12

Percentage of Total Sales to the Government,
NERAC and ARAC Samples

Sample	Number of Firms	Percent of Sample	Percent of Sales
NERAC	13	27.0	0 - 4
	9	18.8	5 - 10
	3	6.3	11 - 19
	13	27.0	20 - 50
	10	20.8	Over 50
ARAC	16	70.0	0 - 4
	4	16.7	5 - 10
	1	4.4	11 - 19
	0	----	20 - 50
	2	8.7	Over 50

Source: Author's data analysis.

TABLE 13

R&D Sales to the Government as Percent of
Total Sales, NERAC and ARAC Samples

Sample	Number of Firms	Percent of Sample	Percent of Sales
NERAC	35	73.0	0 - 4
	3	6.3	5 - 10
	2	4.2	11 - 19
	5	10.4	20 - 50
	3	6.3	Over 50
ARAC	21	91.3	0 - 4
	0	----	5 - 10
	0	----	11 - 19
	0	----	20 - 50
	2	8.7	Over 50

Source: Author's data analysis.

TABLE 14

Total Number of Employees as an Indicator of
Establishment Size, NERAC and ARAC Samples

Sample	Number of Firms	Percent of Sample	Number of Employees
NERAC	14	29.2	0 - 99
	19	39.6	100 - 999
	10	20.8	1,000 -5,000
	5	10.4	Over 5,000
ARAC	0	----	0 - 99
	4	18.2	100 - 999
	7	31.8	1,000 -5,000
	11	50.0	Over 5,000

Source: Author's data analysis.

TABLE 15

Total Sales as an Indicator of Establishment
Size, NERAC and ARAC Samples

Sample	Number of Firms	Percent of Sample	Sales (million dollars)
NERAC	19	18.8	0.2 - .99
	18	37.5	1.2 - 9.9
	17	35.4	10.0 - 100.
	4	8.3	Over 100
ARAC	0	----	0.2 - .99
	4	18.2	1.0 - 9.9
	6	27.1	10.0 - 100.
	12	54.5	Over 100

Note: Five firms did not furnish figures on
their division-level sales, but four of the five did
provide employment figures for the divisions. To
obtain a general idea of sales volume, I multiplied
these employment figures by the average figure for
their industry group and size in the NSF figures.
NSF, Industrial R&D Funds in Relation to Other Economic Variables, NSF 64-25 (Washington, D.C.: U.S.
GPO, October, 1964), p. 36. The one company fur-
nishing neither employment nor sales data is not
represented.

Source: Author's data analysis.

TABLE 16

Sales Growth Rate, NERAC and ARAC Samples
(averaged over the past three years)

Sample	Number of Firms	Percent of Sample	Growth Rate (percent)
NERAC[a]	11	23.4	0 - 2
	5	10.6	3 - 5
	13	27.6	6 - 10
	7	14.9	11 - 20
	11	23.4	Over 21
ARAC[b]	3	20.0	0 - 2
	1	6.7	3 - 5
	3	20.0	6 - 10
	7	47.0	11 - 20
	1	6.7	Over 21

[a]Lincoln Laboratory is not included because its growth rate is set by the government.

[b]Only fifteen ARAC firms answered this question (VIII, 3) on the CQ. Most of the others left it blank or noted that division-level sales was considered proprietary data. Thus, comparisons of the NERAC and ARAC data are not as valid as they might otherwise be.

Source: Author's data analysis.

TABLE 17

Industrial Sample of ARAC Companies

SIC Code	Industrial Group	Number	Percent of Sample
25	Furniture	1	4.4
28	Chemicals	3	13.0
29	Petroleum	1	4.4
30	Rubber	1	4.4
32	Glass	1	4.4
33	Primary metals	1	4.4
35	Machinery, machine tools	3	13.0
36	Electronics	7	30.4
37	Transportation (auto)	5	21.7

Source: Author's data analysis.

Profile of RDC Client Use

Generally, NERAC services were perceived as being rendered in a timely manner; clients also felt that NERAC tried hard to be responsive to client requests. Only five of forty-eight client companies felt that NERAC had not provided good or excellent service or had failed to be responsive to their search requests.*

*All of these five complaints resulted after NERAC changed its sales policy under NASA pressure to procure more lucrative, larger accounts. NERAC then decided not to follow up purchasers of single trial searches.

The forty-eight companies purchased seventy
retrospective searches (RS) and nineteen current
awareness (CA) searches during the first twenty-one
months of NERAC's existence. Most firms (thirty-
nine) purchased only one or two searches, spending
between $150 and $300. This pattern was in line
with NERAC's initial sales approach, which was to
sell their services at a low enough initial price
to attract a large number of trial users. They did
in fact, attract more clients (fifty-four) in their
first year than any other RDC. However, very few
of these trial users (less than 25 percent) renewed
their contracts. As may be seen from Table 18,
there was some relationship between larger-scale
use and renewal. Until recently, ARAC has sold
only larger information packages containing numerous searches and has experienced a high rate of renewal, 58 percent for respondents to this study.[2]

TABLE 18

Number of Searches vs. Renewal, NERAC Sample

Number of Searches	Renew	Possible	No
One	2	13	13
Two	1	4	5
Three or more	6	2	2

Source: Author's data analysis.

Historically ARAC had a renewal rate of about
72 percent among large company subscribers. This
figure differs from the 57 percent figure found for
respondents to this study, but it may be due to a
change in ARAC renewal rate after a five-year trial
was completed in 1968 or to some bias in my sample.
The general policy has been to sell searches only

in large quantities, and initial subscription fees,
until late 1967, were about $3,000 per year. Cost
per search was as low as $75. Thus, subscribers had
an opportunity to sample a wide variety of searches,
and any difficulties in establishing a viable search
strategy could be ironed out.

However, as discussed briefly in Chapter 4,
many ARAC clients may renew their contracts for
reasons other than satisfaction induced by a longer
and more intensive learning period or because of
great interest in space/defense technology. Although it is a difficult hypothesis to substantiate
without more in-depth personal interviews with TU
personnal and ARAC clients, it appears that a significant percentage of ARAC client renewals are due
to a number of factors unrelated to interest in and
usage of aerospace technology. The high ARAC renewal rate appears to be primarily a function of
the following factors (mainly the first two):

1. Commitment to ARAC by management in client
companies

2. Loyalty to the University of Indiana

3. Delay in cancellation, caused by inertia,
once the ARAC contract is approved (in many large
companies

4. Good public relations obtained by participating in a project given extensive national publicity

5. Fear of missing the next "Xerox"

6. Basic inexpensiveness for most of the
large ARAC clients

7. Good ARAC rapport with company information
specialists

8. Provision of a unique resource for those
interested (most of these firms do little business
with the government).

Twenty-nine out of sixty NERAC users completing the SCTQ considered NERAC information to be of some value, although less than 20 percent were willing to place a monetary figure on this "some value" greater than or equal to its cost. (See Table 19.)

TABLE 19

Comparison of Value of NERAC-Supplied
Technology with Its Cost

Written Questionnaires Only		
Information, Alone	Percent of Sample	Comparison
12	20	Cost less than value
6	10	Cost equal to value
23	37.8	Cost greater than value
19	31.8	No answer

Questionnaires and Personal Interviews		
Information, Alone	Percent of Sample	Comparison
12	20	Cost less than value
6	10	Cost equal to value
37	61.7	Cost greater than value
5	8.3	Answer difficult to classify, or not sure

Source: Author's data analysis.

The sixty NERAC users were asked to compare the value of space/defense materials supplied by NERAC with the non-space/defense materials supplied by NERAC. Thirty-five percent of the NERAC users preferred non-space/defense materials, while 15 percent felt the space/defense materials were more valuable and 40 percent thought NERAC information was not useful. (See Tables 20 and 21.) Many more of the NERAC users than of the ARAC users appeared to make use of non-RDC sources of space/defense technical information, 58 percent versus 27 percent. (See Table 22.) Over 29 percent of the ARAC users, on the other hand, felt that space/defense materials were more useful, as against 15 percent of NERAC users.*

Most NERAC users (56 percent) felt that other sources of space/defense technical information were superior. About 43 percent of ARAC users answering this question, on the other hand, appeared to regard ARAC as a superior source. (See Tables 23 and 24.) This comparison must, however, be received with some caution, since only 67 percent of NERAC users answered this question and only 51 percent of ARAC users responded.** The ARAC response is, of course, based solely on mail questionnaire data.

---

*Many NERAC users did not answer these questions on the written SCTQ's, but did answer them during the interview session. Thus, a direct comparison of users in the two samples is difficult unless one assumes that those not answering this question among the ARAC users did not wish to put anything derogatory in writing or simply did not remember the data supplied well enough to respond.

**A very large number of ARAC users apparently do not use other sources of space/defense technical information, since almost 60 percent either said no other sources were used or did not answer this question.

TABLE 20

User Valuation of Space/Defense Technical
Data vs. Non-Space/Defense Technical
Data, NERAC and ARAC Samples

Sample	Number of Users	Percent of Sample	Type of Material Preferred
NERAC	21	35	Open literature-- journals and trade press
	9	15	Space/defense materials, principally searches
	4	6.7	NERAC not useful source
	3	5	Both types equal
	23	38.3	No answer on written questionnaire
ARAC	2	4.9	Open literature-- journals and trade press
	12	29.2	Space/defense materials, principally searches
	6	14.5	ARAC not useful as source
	1	2.4	Both types equal
	20	49.0	No answer on written questionnaire

Source: Author's data compilation.

TABLE 21

NERAC User Valuation of Space/Defense Technical
Data vs. Non-Space/Defense Technical Data

Number of Users	Percent of Sample	Type of Material Preferred
21	35	Open literature-- journals, trade press
9	15	Space/defense materials, principally searches
24	40	NERAC not useful source
3	5	Both types equal
3	5	Answer not classifiable

Source: Author's data analysis.

TABLE 22

Non-RDC Sources of Space/Defense Technology,
NERAC and ARAC Samples

Sample	Number of Users	Percent of Sample	Source of Space/ Defense Technology
NERAC	13	21.6	DDC
	8	13.3	CFSTI
	7	11.7	STAR or NASA Tech Briefs
	8	13.3	Other
	18	30.0	None
	6	10.0	No answer
ARAC	8	19.5	DDC
	2	4.9	CFSTI
	1	2.4	STAR or NASA Tech Briefs
	7	17.0	Other
	6	14.6	None
	18	44.0	No answer

Source: Author's data analysis.

TABLE 23

Comparison of Value of RDC-Supplied Technology
with Other Sources of Space/Defense
Technology, NERAC and ARAC Samples

Sample	Number of Users	Percent of Sample	Comparison
NERAC	8	13.3	NERAC better
	17	28.2	Other sources better
	14	23.2	None useful
	1	1.6	All equally useful
	20	33.3	No answer
ARAC	9	22.0	ARAC better
	7	17.0	Other sources better
	3	7.3	None useful
	2	4.9	All equally useful
	20	49.0	No answer

Source: Author's data analysis.

TABLE 24

Comparison of Value of NERAC-Supplied Technology
with Other Sources of Space/Defense Technology

Number of Users	Percent of Sample	Comparison
8	13.3	NERAC better
34	56.5	Other sources better
14	23.2	None useful
1	1.6	All equally useful
3	5.0	Answer difficult to classify

Source: Author's data analysis.

HORIZONTAL TRANSFER

Transfer and Potential Transfer
of Specific Items

The transfer of specific items of aerospace technology has been advertised by NASA as an integral and necessary result of the public investment in space R&D.[3] Thus, NASA established the RDC's to facilitate and assist in this transfer. The question we are interested in is to what extent these centers have been effective in transferring space/defense technology to commercial/industrial firms.

Seven cases of transfer or potential transfer of specific items of NERAC-supplied technology were uncovered during the course of the fieldwork.*

1.   One small company (under $1 million annual sales) producing electrical components was sent a Tech Brief which may stimulate the manufacture of a new product line of infrared ovens.[4]

2.   A Route 128 high-technology company (annual sales of $3.5 million) received a report as part of an RS which immediately led to exploring a subcontract with a local aerospace firm for a new sealing material.

3.   One very large NERAC client ($1.1 billion annual sales in 1969) received the name of a possible subcontractor for a new electro-mechanical

---

*One additional potential transfer of space/defense technology was found, but resulted from a yearly subscription to NASA Tech Briefs, not from NERAC-supplied material. However, it generally confirms Hypothesis 3, in that this very small firm (sales in 1967 of about $500,000) sells technically sophisticated medical instrumentation and two of its ten staff members are engineers.

development project. The potential subcontractor
was himself a NERAC client.

4.-5. Two companies, one a large camera manufacturer and one a very small manufacturer of electrical components (annual sales under $700,000),
used the results of several RS's to assist in the
successful defense of patent infringement suits.

These five examples of transfer all involved
aerospace technology; the next two are not clearly
examples of horizontal transfer, but are included
as examples of the more general role an RDC may play
as agent in stimulating transfer at many levels and
perhaps providing a generally more hospitable environment for the transfer of externally created
technology.

6. A central Massachusetts manufacturer of
paper-making machinery located five MIT-developed
computer programs on stress analysis through the
personal assistance and counseling of a NERAC engineer.*

7. A division of a large chemical firm (annual
corporate sales of more than $1.5 billion and annual
division sales of $20 million) received some material
from the open chemical literature which was directly
applied to the development of a new material.**

----

*Such on-site personal assistance is no longer
part of the NERAC service package. This transfer
resulted primarily through the personal knowledge
and MIT contacts of the particular AE involved.
The programs may have been written under space/
defense funding at MIT.

**The information was from several chemical
trade journals obtained by NERAC from the Institute
for Scientific Information, and contained no space/
defense-supported R&D results.

Thus, of the forty-eight companies interviewed, one in seven, or about 14.6 percent, could recall an actual or potential transfer that had resulted directly from NERAC-supplied material. Of these seven examples only three, the two patent infringement background materials and the background on a new chemical development, have actually been used. The other four have not yet been applied, but appear to have the potential of being applied.

The two largest users of RDC services in New England were a large consulting firm and a medium-size electronics firm, both located in the greater Boston area.

NASA financed a study of possible transfer of aerospace technology for developing countries, paying for over $5,000 worth of searches from two RDC's. The searches were to form the basis of the transferrable data base. The study concluded that under the right conditions there might be some possibility of transfer to underdeveloped countries.

From conversations with the project chief and two other project members at ADL, it appeared that none of the researchers considered the NASA Tapes as important sources of technical information and used them only because it was a contract requirement. They all relied on the in-house literature searching group for all their other technical literature requirements.

The other large user purchased a $4,000 annual membership from the University of Pittsburgh RDC, the Knowledge Availability Systems Center (KASC). A poll was taken of the company users after the year was over, and it was found that of thirty-nine users, twenty-three recommended discontinuing, eleven recommended continuing, two were undecided, and three could not be reached. The membership in KASC was not renewed, but NERAC was able to sell the same purchaser several searches. It was generally agreed by the technologist who used both KASC and NERAC that NERAC service was better and more responsive (poor service had been a common complaint about KASC). However, he felt that the service was generally not as useful as interpersonal contacts and informal means of communication both within and without the company for obtaining new technical information of relevance for him.

The ARAC mail survey turned up one example of specific item transfer among the twenty-three firms who returned the questionnaires, and two other firms mentioned that they had made some general use of ARAC-supplied materials as background for new product development. Firms may, however, be generally reluctant to be very specific about new product ideas in writing. Thus, it is hard to compare the NERAC and ARAC data in this area.* ARAC performed a survey of its clients for possible transfer and turned up twenty-five items, but their definition of transfer for the study was more general than that used here, and the survey covered a five-year period (1963-68).**

A letter from the ARAC Assistant Director, dated February 28, 1969, indicated that they had not yet been able to identify any "major" items of transfer (in six years of operation).

To place some quantitative value on the NERAC transfers, clients were asked to compare the cost of the information or services supplied by NERAC

---

*One additional example of transfer was uncovered, but it was a vertical transfer item. A large space/defense contractor was led to another contractor's low-temperature plastic for cryogenic application, and this development was applied in space/defense work. However, this client did not perceive the transfer to be of great value.

**A detailed comparison of their results is given in Chapter 2, section entitled "ARAC/NERAC Studies."

with their value.[5] Client companies were also asked
to indicate the cost of reviewing RDC-supplied materials. The seven NERAC clients who reported a specific item transfer or potential transfer indicated
that they had spent about twenty man-days reviewing
the materials supplied by NERAC, which would add
something to the cost figure of $4,160. The one
ARAC client indicated an annual review cost of
about twelve man-days. Of course, these review
costs are the total man-days spent in the year to
review all ARAC-supplied literature, not just the
one item, and no investment costs were given.

Apparently, little or no investment has yet
been made in any of these transfers or potential
transfers aside from RDC fees and review costs,
since none of the clients was able to provide any
data on additional investment costs. The ADL experimental transfer project indicated that their
four transfers involved "low-cost items."

Also, clients were asked to evaluate cost-
effectiveness during the interview session whenever
a transfer was identified. The seven client companies paid NERAC approximately $4,160 for the tech-
nical data or services which resulted in the transfers and estimated that they spent about twenty man-
days in reviewing the materials internally. They
estimated the value of the information and services
to be $37,000. One company's value of $25,000 for
tne non-aerospace, open-literature chemical data
represents the bulk of this value figure. On the
other hand, none of the potential transfers was
valued at less than its cost; and should the transfers actually be accomplished they would swell the
value figure considerably. The one potential ARAC
transfer was valued at $400 versus a cost for ARAC
services of $175.

To place these figures in context, it should
be noted that NASA had directly funded NERAC during
this period (twenty-one months) to the extent of
$440,000 (1.75 x $250,000/year).[6] This figure does
not include any of the other costs to NASA of main-
taining this RDC such as acquisition of technical

data, contract administration, or technical supervision. Nor do these value figures include all the
other general background technology supplied by
NERAC to other clients not included in the definition of specific item transfer. Over 50 percent of
all users of NERAC technology perceived it to be of
some value to them. Also, given the long time
periods involved in transfer, it is not possible to
evaluate NERAC's effectiveness as a transfer agent
solely on the basis of short-term direct transfer
values.

Although a sample of seven transfers (from the
seventy-one sampled companies) hardly represents
statistically conclusive evidence, it does generally lend some validity to the hypotheses stated in
Chapter 3. The small number of specific item transfers is generally in line with the first hypothesis,
which predicted that very little transfer could be
identified after so short a time. The paucity of
specific item transfers and the fact that no entrepreneurial, market-oriented approach was attempted
also lends some validity to the fourth hypothesis,
which predicted that very few specific item transfers were likely to occur.[7]

The circumstances surrounding these cases
lends some validity to the second hypothesis, which
states that transfer of space/defense technology
(or any other highly sophisticated technology) is
more likely where the company has a highly sophisticated technical base.* Five of the seven companies
had a ratio of R&D technologists to total employees
of 10 percent or greater, and spent in excess of

---

*Sophisticated technical base is defined for
this study in terms of a high ratio of R&D technologists to total employment and of R&D spending
to sales, sophistication of product lines, the
presence of a separate R&D function not tied to an
operating division, and a large percentage of sales
in the space/defense market.

10 percent of sales on R&D. Six of the seven companies sell sophisticated product lines, five in
electronics and instrumentation and one in new plastics and other hydrocarbons. Five of the seven companies sold 20 percent or more of their products in
the space/defense market. The only company that
did not fit the pattern ranked low in all areas
associated with a sophisticated technical base, but
was in the process of upgrading its technical capac-
ity and had just hired a number of new technologists.

Other Sources of Transfer

Question V on the CQ asked client companies to
specify other sources of space/defense technology
which had resulted in actual or planned transfer.
This question was used to compare NERAC, and RDC's
generally, with other sources of transferrable technology.

None of the interviewees could place an exact
figure on the amount of transfer from other sources
of space/defense technology. However, it is possible to infer from their answers to this question,
and from other studies, some general idea about the
extent of in-house transfer by the sample companies.

First, three companies were common to both this
study and to the spin-off studies of Roberts. These
companies have averaged over 40 percent transfer
from their initial space/defense market during the
last five years. The transfer mechanism was primarily technologist mobility and internal technical
entrepreneurship, rather than literature dissemination.[8] Technical mobility, as a transfer mechanism,
is defined as the movement of a space/defense technologist from one organization (profit, non-profit,
or governmental) to another (limited to profit-
making organizations) which results in the development and sale of a new product or products for commercial end use. The technologist may bring with
him either a specific item or items of space/defense
technology or a specialized expertise which is directly applied to new product development; this new

product development would most likely not have taken
place without the movement of the technologist from
one organization to another.

Technical entrepreneurship, as a transfer mechanism, is defined as the transfer of a new item or
items of aerospace technology by means of the ini-
tiative of an individual acting as a "champion"
within an existing organization or, more often, by
an individual's leaving an existing organization
(profit, non-profit, or governmental) and forming a
new company.

The 40 percent transfer rate refers to transfer
of space/defense technology by these MIT spin-off
firms, through the mechanisms of technologist mobility or technical entrepreneurship or both; the items
transferred resulted proximately from the space/
defense products initially sold exclusively for government (or government contractor) end use. Of
course, some adaptation was required for commercial
sales.

Roberts allowed me to compare my results with
his files on these three companies--one was spun
off from the MIT Instrumentation Laboratory, one
from the MIT Electrical Engineering Department, and
one from the MIT Lincoln Laboratory.

Eight of the remaining forty-five NERAC clients
sell over half of their output in the space/defense
market.* Four of these eight companies had established substantial areas of transfer from their
space/defense technology base, mainly in the last
five years. The average was about 5 percent of
their present sales. The transfer mechanism was
primarily internal commercial diversification.
None of the interviewees could remember the precise
origin of externally generated technology in the

----

*Two of the spin-off companies also sell over
50 percent of their output in the space/defense
market.

transfer process, and the exact sequence of events
is apparently lost in the corporate antiquity.*

Twelve other firms sold between 20 and 50 percent of their products and services in the government market and mainly for space/defense application.** All but one of these firms indicated transfer to the commercial market over the last five
years. Six of these firms which had been substantially 100 percent government contractors at the
time of their founding shifted to over 50 percent
commercial sales within the last six years. While
the other three had not experienced such substantial
commercial transfer, they averaged over 10 percent
during the last five years. Some of the interviewees were vague about transfer mechanisms, but over
half the firms had most of the characteristics of
the MIT spin-off firms except the origin of their

---

*One of the larger companies has been spurred
to transfer for at least three identifiable reasons:
1. Acquisition of several consumer product
companies had provided a market for some of its
space/defense technology.
2. Trends in space/defense spending during
the early 1960's had created some pressure to smooth
yearly sales figures through the development of more
stable commercial markets.
3. There was the need to promote some spin-
offs from its space R&D contracts for public relations purposes.
Data for these conclusions came from interviews with an engineer-manager and chief of public
relations, January, 1969.

**One firm, a manufacturer of civil engineering
implements, sold 30 percent of its output to the
Department of the Interior and the Corps of Engineers; all the others sold almost exclusively in
the space/defense market. One of the spin-off
firms sells between 20 and 50 percent of its output in the space/defense market, making a total of
thirteen firms in this 20 to 50 percent category.

founders. Technologist mobility and technical entrepreneurship were the primary mechanisms discussed,
and none mentioned literature dissemination as important for transfer.

Most of the twenty-three firms* that had experienced extensive transfer also had another dis-
tinguishing characteristic besides extensive sales
in the space/defense market: only two of them had
total sales exceeding $10 million. Almost all of
these small firms had most of the characteristics of
a technically based "Boston 128"-type spin-off company.

Twenty-two of the twenty-five remaining firms
could not recall substantial amounts of transfer
from any sources of space/defense technology.**
Three of the specific item NERAC technology transfers occurred among the remaining firms; two of
these firms, the plastics division of a large chemical company and a large camera manufacturer, provided exceptionally receptive encironments for the
transfer of externally generated technology.[9] These
two firms both maintained extensive R&D facilities;
organizationally one was a central R&D facility for
the company, while the other was part of an operating division. However, the latter R&D organization contained a large number of physical science
Ph.D.'s and was, therefore, most receptive to externally generated technology.

None of the twenty-three ARAC firms completing
questionnaires could recall transfer from any other

_____

*The twenty-three firms include the three MIT
spin-offs; eight firms sold over 50 percent to government directly or indirectly.

**None of these firms sold more than 19 percent
of its output to the government, and twenty-one
sold less than 10 percent to the government directly or indirectly.

sources of space/defense technology. However, only two of these firms participated very heavily in the space/defense market, and none had more than one or two of the characteristics of a sophisticated technically based company.*

Thus transfer of space/defense technology by the sampled companies was found primarily among companies that participate substantially in the space/defense market, have a sophisticated technical base, and are relatively small.

IMPLICATIONS OF THE FINDINGS
FOR HYPOTHESES

The first hypothesis was that it is unlikely that much transfer has occurred as a result of the NASA Dissemination program.** To support this hypothesis, the following evidence is submitted:

1. Only 14.6 percent of the NERAC sample (seven of forty-eight) alluded to specific transfer.

2. Only one of twenty-three clients alluded to transfer.

3. A low value was placed on services provided. Only 20 percent of the NERAC sample considered value to be greater than cost.

4. Most NERAC users felt other sources of technology were superior to those supplied by NERAC.

---

*One firm is a large space/defense division of a $2 billion-plus corporation, and the other is a $25 million government contractor.

**Three other studies of RDC effectiveness provide some additional evidence to support hypothesis 1. See Ch. 2, sections entitled "Surveys of RDC Effectiveness" and "ARAC/NERAC Studies."

Seven cases of specific item transfer or potential transfer were uncovered in the course of the
fieldwork with forty-eight NERAC clients, or 14.6
percent of the companies. Five of the transfers or
potential transfers were from space/defense technology. The other two were from more general sources
of scientific and technical information. Only one
example of specific item transfer was recorded by
the twenty-three ARAC clients returning questionnaires.

The responses discussed thus far were to specific questions on the CQ (no. IV) and on the SCTQ
requesting that any actual or planned transfer occurring as a result of RDC-supplied information be
indicated. Questions 14 and 15 on the SCTQ attempted
to measure transfer more indirectly by asking users
to compare the value of the information (question 14)
and/or services (question 15) received with their
cost. Only six NERAC clients had received any services other than selective mail dissemination of
technical information. Of the six, only three felt
the services were worth more than they cost. ARAC
supplies only selective technical information, mainly through company libraries.

Thus, many more users were able to respond to
the question comparing the value of the information
with its cost. Twelve NERAC users felt the information supplied was more valuable than its cost. Six
of the twelve are included in the transfer or potential transfer group. The other six felt the information was particularly useful for such reasons as
background for technical articles, library building
in a very specialized area (ratchets), and as background for technical problem solving (four of six).

Thus, the responses to questions 14 and 15 generally indicate that most NERAC clients place a low
value on the services and information supplied,
which provides some additional evidence of the low
rate of transfer resulting from the NERAC services
or information. The ARAC respondents showed a
corresponding lack of enthusiasm for RDC information

when asked to quantify their perception of value
versus cost. However, almost two-thirds of the ARAC
users were unwilling to compare their perception of
value with cost and put it in writing.* Generally,
the forty-one ARAC users did not answer question 14
(63.5 percent). Of those that did answer, opinions
were divided on the issue of value versus cost. Apparently most users of ARAC technology are not aware
of its cost, since it is paid out of corporate library funds. Also, there appears to be great reluctance to reduce an intangible such as the value of
technical information to a monetary figure, or to
make potentially derogatory remarks in writing.
The reluctance to make this comparison may indicate
a general uncertainty about the dollar value of ARAC
information. In the NERAC sample it was possible to
avoid this reluctance to place a dollar value on the
information in writing by discussing the question
during the interview session.

Another indirect measure of value was the question which asked users to compare the value of RDC-
supplied space/defense technology with other sources.
Most NERAC users felt other sources were superior to
NERAC. Only 13.3 percent felt that NERAC was superior to other sources, who answered this question,
favored ARAC slightly; but, as with question 14,
many ARAC users were not able or did not wish to
make this comparison between ARAC and other sources.

One problem with these two indirect measures
of transfer is exactly how to relate user perceptions of value to transfer or potential transfer.

---

*This reluctance to compare value with cost
may also be partially due to an unwillingness to
give a negative appraisal when management is already committed to the service. NERAC client management, on the other hand, generally was not committed to continuing the service, and thus users
may have felt more freedom to respond to this question.

User perceptions of value appear to vary according to the completeness of transfer. Where the transfer is far advanced, the user is usually able and willing to place a monetary value on the technology being applied, but when the transfer is less certain or bound up in a complex process involving many elements, users are apparently unable or unwilling to place a quantitative value on it.

Some additional evidence to support this hypothesis is provided by several studies of technological diffusion which indicate that industrial diffusion is generally a slow process, often requiring twenty years or more from the inception of a new item of technology to its general adoption.[10] Further, the study by Sumner Myers and his colleagues at NPA indicates that innovations that they found which had originated in space/defense technology were generally more complex, were on a larger scale, and required a larger investment to bring to the point of commercial application than comparable innovations which had their origin in commercially developed technology.[11] Thus, one would expect that the transfer or diffusion of aerospace innovations might require even more time for widespread commercial usage than would innovations originating from commercial/industrial R&D. Since the NASA TUP has been in existence only since 1963, one would not, a priori, expect to find that a large amount of transfer had occurred, given these research findings about the transfer process.

The second hypothesis was that transfer of space/defense technology to private industry is likely to occur only where the company has a highly sophisticated technical base. Evidence to support this hypothesis is the following:

1. Five of seven companies which alluded to specific item transfer had a ratio of R&D technologists to total employees of 10 percent or greater. Also, R&D expenditures were greater than 10 percent of sales.

2. Six of the seven companies sell technically sophisticated product lines.

3. Five of the seven companies sold 20 percent or more of their products in the space/defense market.

4. The seventh company was in the process of substantially upgrading its technical base.

5. Of the twelve users who perceived NERAC technology as more valuable than cost, all but one had a highly sophisticated technological base.

6. All of the companies that renewed their contract with NERAC were technically sophisticated. (The ARAC sample results are at variance with this result.)

As noted earlier in the chapter, six of the seven specific item transfers or potential transfers were made to companies with a highly sophisticated technical base.

Another measure of the validity of hypothesis 2 is a check on which type of companies perceived NERAC-supplied technology as most valuable.* Of the twelve users who perceived NERAC technology as more valuable than cost, all but one came from establishments which had a highly sophisticated technical base.

Another indirect measure of transfer is receptivity and interest in externally generated technology. The study used client willingness to renew contracts (for the same level or a higher level of services) as some indicator of receptivity to NERAC-supplied technology.[12] To check on user interest

---

*Four other studies on technological transfer bear out the second hypotheses: Marquis-Roberts, Shimshoni, and ADL.

TABLE 25

Client Satisfaction vs. Renewal

	Renewal	Percent	Possible Renewal	Percent	No Renewal	Percent
Very satisfied	14	21	2	3		
Satisfied	7	10.5	9	13	3	4.5
Neutral			9	13	2	3.0
Dissatisfied			2	3	20	30.0
Total	21	31.5	22	32	25	37.5

Note: Renewal is defined as actual renewal of services at the same or a higher level of usage or the expressed intent so to renew. Possible renewal is defined to mean an expressed general satisfaction with NERAC services, coupled with an intent to renew only if a specific need arose for NERAC services. No Renewal is defined to mean that the client perceived NERAC-supplied technology as irrelevant to his needs.

Source: Author's data analysis.

146

and receptivity to RDC-supplied technology, a number of questions, both during the interview and on
the written SCTQ, asked the interviewees to state
their satisfaction (questions 4 and 5) or what
monetary value they would place on the information
or services provided (questions 14 and 15).   Propensity to renew contracts with RDC's was also
checked during the question-and-answer sessions.
It was quite simple to check client renewal for ARAC
by examining a final report which included a table
of client renewal history since the center's inception.

There was a clear relation between the industrial group to which the NERAC client belonged and
its propensity to renew. As shown in Table 26,
roughly one-third of the chemical and electronics
groups are in the process of renewing or have already renewed their use of NERAC services, while
not one company in the machine tool, fabricated
metals, or primary metals groups has renewed. This
is an interesting result, since a high percentage
of NASA publications are tailored for use in metals
and machinery areas,* and it appears to indicate
that propensity to renew was closely related to technical sophistication of the client.**   (See Tables
27, 28, and 29.)

-----

*Published Tech Briefs in the "mechanical"
area (machine tools, shop techniques, and some
metals) constituted 29 percent of the total as of
mid-1969. An equally large percentage of NASA Special Reports are in functional areas of interest to
the machine tool group.

**The eight machinery, machine tool, and machine
tool component manufacturers that form part of the
NERAC sample generally perceived space/defense technology as irrelevant to their new technology needs
now and for the indefinite future. This response
nicely illustrates the result expected of a mature
industrial group to externally generated technology
and agrees quite well with Schon's studies of industrial innovation. See Donald Schon, Technology and
Change (New York: Delacorte Press, 1967), pp. 139-71,
particularly pp. 151-55.

TABLE 26

Client Industrial Group vs. Renewal,
NERAC and ARAC Samples

SIC Code	Industrial Group	NERAC R	P	N	Total in Each Group
28	Chemicals	2	2	1	5
33	Primary metals		1		1
34	Fabricated metals		3	3	6
35	Machinery tools and components		3	5	8
36, 38	Electronics and instrumentation Non-metallic materials	7	8	10	25
39	Miscellaneous	1		2	3

SIC Code	Industrial Group	ARAC R	P	N	Total in Each Group
05	Furniture			1	1
28	Chemicals		1	2	3
29	Petroleum	1			1
30	Rubber	1			1
32	Glass	1			1
33	Primary metals	1			1
35	Machinery, machine tools	3	1	2	3
36	Electronics	5		2	7
37	Transportation (4 auto and 1 railroad)	4		1	5

Note: R = Renewal.
P = Possible Renewal.
N = No Renewal.

Source: Author's data analysis.

148

TABLE 27

Renewal vs. Type of Company

Type of Company	Renewal	Possible Renewal	No Renewal
Route 128 type (13)	4 (38%)	6 (46%)	2 (15%)
Others (35)	5 (14%)	11 (31%)	19 (54%)

Source: Author's data analysis.

TABLE 28

Technologist Ratio vs. Renewal,
NERAC and ARAC Samples

Sample	Technologist Ratio as Percent of Total Employment	Renewal	Possible Renewal
NERAC	0 - 5	2	10
	5 - 14	5	6
	15 - 21	3	2
ARAC	0 - 5	9	2
	5 - 14	2	-
	15 - 21	2	-

Source: Author's data analysis.

TABLE 29

Separate R&D Function vs. Renewal,
NERAC and ARAC Samples

Sample	Separate R&D Function	Renewal	Possible Renewal	No Renewal
NERAC	Separate	8	10	7
	Too small for separate functional units*	1	4	1
	Not separate	1	5	11
ARAC	Separate	9	1	4
	Too small for separate functional units*	-	1	-
	Not separate	4	3	1

*These companies performed a large percentage of R&D, but are too small to have a separate laboratory.

Source: Author's data analysis.

The ARAC client companies generally showed somewhat different relationships between renewals and industrial grouping. The three chemical companies were not particularly interested in continuing their relationships, but two of the three were primarily in ethical drugs, not chemicals; also, four automobile component manufacturers were represented in the ARAC sample, and three of the four had renewed their services. These three companies indicated that they found little useful material in the ARAC-supplied technology, but continued because they were fearful of "missing something." The one company in the auto group which cancelled its ARAC membership indicated that it would rather "miss something" than spend the time reviewing ARAC-supplied materials.

In the ARAC sample, with an overall positive renewal rate of 57 percent (thirteen of twenty-three), only four or five of the thirteen renewals could be classed as belonging to a high technology industrial group. Nor would more than four or five of the companies qualify as being technically sophisticated by spin-off company standards. However, seven of the thirteen were the central R&D laboratories of the corporations and two were functionally separate R&D organizations in space/defense contractors. Two of the remaining four were continuing their membership with ARAC despite their feeling that the information was not very relevant. The other two ARAC renewals were companies with low technology bases which would not have been predicted as likely clients for space/defense technology.

Of course, renewal may occur for a variety of reasons quite unrelated to transfer or potential transfer. Still, the ARAC data do not clearly support the notion that renewal will always be directly related to the technical sophistication of the client firm.*

The third hypothesis was that it is likely that smaller, technically based firms, such as the Boston Route 128-type spin-off firms, have more readily accepted and used the services of the NASA

---

*See Ch. 4, section entitled "NERAC and ARAC: Major Similarities and Differences of Two RDC's," for a discussion of many of the reasons for the high ARAC renewal rate.

RDC's.* To support this hypothesis, the following
evidence is submitted:

1. Six of ten NERAC renewals fit the description of the Boston Route 128-type spin-off firms.

2. Five of the other seven spin-off-type firms
said they would renew whenever they had a problem
that warranted the use of NERAC-supplied technology.

As noted in the discussion of the second hypothesis, one measure of receptivity to NERAC-
supplied technology is willingness to renew contracts for services. Ten of the forty-eight companies had already renewed or intended to do so.
Six of these ten would fit the definition of a Boston Route 128-type spin-off company, and four would
not. Of the four who would not fit the definition,
two are the research laboratories of large commercial corporate divisions using NERAC, not for space/
defense technology but for general chemical technology. One of the other two is the research laboratory of a large camera manufacturer, and the last is
a large non-profit R&D laboratory.

Seven other Route 128-type companies are represented in the sample. Five of these indicated that
they would renew their contracts whenever they had
a problem that warranted the use of NERAC-supplied
technology. The other two firms felt that very
little state-of-the-art material was reported by
space/defense contractors or otherwise appeared in
the open literature; and since their work was all

---

*It did not appear from the ARAC questionnaires
that any of the responding companies would qualify
as a spin-off-type company for the purposes of this
study. There is some indication of confirmation of
hypothesis 3 from the innovation studies by Roberts
and Shimshoni discussed in Ch. 2, sections entitled
"Marquis-Roberts Spin-off Studies" and "Shimshoni
Study."

state-of-the-art, NERAC-supplied materials were not
sufficiently timely, nor did they contain any new
technology for these companies.* Thus, response of
the Route 128-type companies to renewal was considerably above that of the overall sample.

The fourth hypothesis was that the transfer of
general background information is more likely than
specific invention transfer. To support this hypothesis, consider the following evidence:

1. There were only seven cases of specific
item transfer.

2. Seventy-seven percent of companies claimed
that NERAC provided background information useful
in the preparation of technical proposals or reports,
or for general technical problem solving.

3. Eighty-three percent of ARAC sample indicated that the materials were used for general background information.

Most of those firms renewing their contracts
with NERAC have not participated in any specific
item transfer or any potential specific item transfer. Moreover, the vast majority of clients indicated that their primary use for NERAC technology
was to provide background information in preparation
of technical proposals or reports, or for technical
problem solving (thirty-seven of forty-eight, or 77
percent).** ARAC clients also indicated their major

_____

*They also felt that companies simply withheld
all important new developments until they would no
longer lose any competitive advantage by reporting
them. These companies relied almost entirely on
personal contacts with customers, vendors, consultants, and the local technical community for new
technology.

**The ADL study also tends to confirm hypothesis
4. See Ch. 2, section entitled "Arthur D. Little
Study."

use was to provide general stimulus (nineteen of
twenty-three firms, or 83 percent).*   (See Table 30.)

TABLE 30

Use of RDC-Supplied Materials,
NERAC and ARAC Samples

Use	Percentage
NERAC	
Background	33
To find out what had been done	33
To find out who had done work	25
None	25
ARAC	
Background	63
To find out what had been done	48
To find out who had done work	10
None	12

Note: Some multiple answers were given.

Sources: DRI, The Commercial Applications of
Missile/Space Technology, NASA-sponsored report
(Springfield, Va.:   CFSTI, 1963); and NPA, "Technology Transfer and Industrial Innovation," unpublished report prepared for NSF by Sumner Myers,
et al. (Washington, D.C.:   NSF, February, 1967).

----

*Twenty-three of forty-eight NERAC companies
also used the material as background for planning
and eight used it as a general stimulus.

The fifth hypothesis was that NASA policies curbing entrepreneurial activities and requiring self-sufficiency within three to five years have had the effect of inhibiting useful transfer experiments. In order to prove this hypothesis, we will separate it into two parts, as follows:

1. NASA policies inhibiting entrepreneurial activities and requiring self-sufficiency within three to five years have largely restricted RDC information diffusion efforts to routinized channels within client companies, such as libraries or technical information centers.

2. Restricting information diffusion to routinized information channels within client companies has had the effect of inhibiting useful transfer experiment.

The initial NERAC approach to operations was two-pronged: on the one hand, to provide information services needed for technologists to maintain awareness in their specialized interest area and, on the other hand, to assist clients in adapting space/defense technology for commercial application.[13] The first aim of the service package was to provide the standardized RDC approach to selective dissemination of technical information through the use of one-shot RS's and monthly CA's. The second was to provide continuing contact and counseling of client companies by the applications engineers (AE's). The AE was to develop an innovation profile of each client, including an analysis of intra-firm communication, new product decision making, and an identification of corporate innovation needs.

Needless to say, this second part of the NERAC approach might have been expensive to implement in comparison with the cost of supplying selective technical literature searches. Also, to be effective it would require contact with a variety of corporate personnel and would be similar to new product consulting. It would also have required that the AE assume the role of a product champion until he could identify such a champion within the client company.

During the first six months of NERAC operation, this interpersonal contact was tried on a limited scale in Massachusetts. It was soon curtailed because it was felt to be too expensive per short-term sales dollar, given the NASA-imposed requirement for rapid production of a substantial amount of industrial sales. There is, of course, no way of determining whether such an interpersonal approach would have resulted in a substantial amount of transfer. However, two of the specific item transfers were the result of the one AE operating in Massachusetts, and several other companies presented potential opportunities for transfer.

The data indicate that the present focus of NERAC is on selective dissemination of technical literature to larger companies through routinized technical information channels. The only interpersonal contact is that of an initial sales presentation which is occasionally followed up at the end of the contract year. These contracts are strictly sales-oriented, with no transfer activities involved.

ARAC clients likewise indicated that almost all contracts were through their in-house libraries, and they rarely saw ARAC personnel after the initial sales presentation. ARAC indicates that budgetary constraints have made anything but selective information dissemination too expensive.[14]

NASA has even required in several contracts that RDC's place their major emphasis on the establishment of routinized channels of dissemination within client companies.[15] From interviews with personnel at four RDC's, the TUD Director, and other TU personnel, it was clear that the major thrust of RDC transfer efforts was to be on dissemination of printed matter to company libraries and information centers.* These interviews and follow-up discussions

---

*Interviews conducted between June, 1966 and February, 1969.

indicated a policy against the use of market-
oriented interpersonal transfer methods. Further,
the response of the TUP to the experimental market-
oriented, entrepreneurial transfer program initiated by ADL in 1964 was to cancel the program after
only a few months, despite indications of some successful transfers.[16]

There is less direct evidence to prove the
second part of the hypothesis, but a number of
studies indicate that horizontal transfer is unlikely to occur as a result of the dissemination of
technical reports and studies alone; rather, transfer results more from interpersonal contact on a
continuing basis.[17] Other studies indicate that
innovators generally do not work through established
corporate channels of communication.[18] Still other
studies indicate that transfer, particularly horizontal transfer of space/defense technology, is a
complex problem; we have very little hard data that
would indicate how programs directed at transfer
should be structured to maximize their effectiveness.[19] Thus, much more empirical evidence is
needed before we can confidently establish firm
policies for the operation of transfer centers.

This overall hypothesis is quite difficult to
prove in any final sense, since many programs and
experiments that might otherwise have been tried,
have simply never been done. The centers have not
provided any systematic feedback system, which is
crucial to meaningful transfer of any kind, short-
term or long-term, whether through document dissemination or otherwise. The reasons are generally the
following:[20]

1. The commitment that NERAC as an RDC will
have developed a clientele and income level such
that it will be self-sufficient with respect to
NASA support for operating expenses within three
years dictates that its major, if not exclusive,
effort be directed at securing and cultivating or
strengthening relations with clients for its search
and information services.

2. The study of the technology transfer process is not apparently regarded by NASA as a separate and parallel program objective.

3. Effective NERAC/client relations appear to discourage any use of client organizations as "laboratories" for the purpose of studying the transfer and utilization process for two reasons:

    a. Efforts to make sales and secure the use of NERAC's services are difficult enough, and added activity might upset a delicate relationship;

    b. Effective transfer agents and data users who would be most helpful would be likely to be those most "vital" to their employers and men who should not be bothered.

CONCLUSIONS, LIMITATIONS, AND IMPLICATIONS FOR FURTHER STUDY

Conclusions

The following conclusions were reached:

1. Firms that use the RDC's and consider them important sources of aerospace technology are few in number and have a sophisticated technical base, as measured by most of the following factors:

    a. High ratio of R&D technologists to total employment

    b. High percentage of performance R&D

    c. Separate R&D function

    d. Membership in a high technology industrial group

    e. Performance of a large percentage of their business for the government.

2.   Some commercial firms not having a highly
sophisticated technical base made use of the RDC's
for general technical literature (mainly non-space/
defense) and/or because of inertia or because they
fear missing some really great new invention.

3.   Little specific item transfer has occurred,
and technical literature dissemination does not appear to have been an effective method of promoting
specific item transfer.

4.   Generally, RDC services are perceived as
rapid, efficient, and responsive to client firm requests within the technical capabilities of their
staffs and their data base. However, the fact that
NERAC and the other RDC's resort to technical data
sources other than the NASA data tapes over 50 percent of the time indicates that this aerospace data
base is not considered the bonanza to commercial
industry envisaged by NASA.

5.   Most firms that make use of these two RDC's
do not consider them (or aerospace technology generally) as an important source of new technology for
their immediate business needs, though some firms
do indicate that in the long term they expect some
spin-off or spillover to occur, but are vague as to
content or timing.

6.   Smaller Route 128-type contractors among
the NERAC sample were receptive to RDC services,
since they typically do not have an extensive technical information system in-house and may have to
go through a prime contractor to establish a need-
to-know to gain access to government information.

7.   RDC pricing and marketing policies have
had some effect on company acceptance and use.
NERAC began with a very low piecework charge which
quickly resulted in over fifty clients, but found
that this did not generate enough income to please
the TUP; therefore the policy was changed to yearly
memberships, which may have created market resis-
tance in some firms. Also, single trials appear to
be ineffectual in gaining continuing use.

8. ARAC marketing strategy, based on larger-scale company commitments, has been a far more effective method of obtaining and retaining large industrial clients. Situs university assistance appears to be most important in obtaining local industrial support.

9. RDC-supplied information has benerally been used as background information for technical problem solving, not for new product ideas. Some firms have used it to find out what others have done in a given area or for proposal preparation.

10. Neither of these RDC's has been cost-effective in terms of user appraisal of services, renewals, or measurable dollar-valued end products.

Limitations of Fieldwork

Limitations of the fieldwork were the following:

1. Only about one-sixth (48 of 303) of all RDC industrial clients were interviewed in person, and companies seemed generally reluctant to provide much information in writing which was either derogatory to the RDC's or touched upon areas considered proprietary, such as division-level sales or growth rates and new product planning or development.

2. Technologists appeared to be reluctant to place a monetary value on the technology supplied by an RDC, especially when the only contact was through written questionnaires.

3. While the personal interviews sample was reasonably representative of New England manufacturers, it was not entirely representative of total RDC client composition.

4. RDC's have been in existence only a few years, and the diffusion process is quite slow--possibly even slower for aerospace technology transfer to commercial industry; thus, later studies may reveal different transfer rates.

5. On the basis of the data gathered, it was not possible to completely explain the disparity between NERAC and ARAC client renewal rates, or the relatively higher rate of satisfaction indicated in the ARAC mail questionnaires.

Implications for Future Study

The major focus of the NASA RDC program has always been on literature dissemination. This literature dissemination was not found to have produced very much short-term transfer, but it may have a cumulative educational impact, stimulating greater long-term receptivity to sophisticated technology among RDC clients. Thus it may be worthwhile to examine RDC client transfer over a longer time period to determine whether the RDC literature dissemination will play any long-term role in stimulating transfer.

The fieldwork results indicated that some ARAC clients appeared willing to invest substantial sums of money in RDC information services even though they did not feel that the technology they received was relevant to their present market needs. A number of tentative explanations were offered for this phenomenon, but some additional study is needed to pinpoint more specifically the reasons for this willingness of some RDC clients to invest. Such a study may provide some insights for structuring other federal transfer programs, such as the Department of Commerce's State Technical Services Program, to obtain interested and continuing industrial participation.

NOTES

1. This definition describes the average spin-off firm studied by Roberts, but the physical location and affiliation of the founders may be different in the two samples. See Edward Roberts and Herbert Wainer, "Technology Transfer and Entrepreneurial Success," paper presented to the Twentieth

National Conference on the Administration of Research, Miami Beach, Florida, October 26, 1966.

2. See ARAC, Final Five Year Report, Experiment to Transfer Technology from a University-Based Center, report prepared under NASA contract SC-NASr-162 (Bloomington, Ind.: ARAC, February, 1968), pp. 18-32.

3. All of the Congressional hearings on the TUP from the inception of the program place great stress on the transfer of specific items of aerospace technology to commercial industry. The discussion in Samuel Doctors, The Role of the Federal Agencies in Technology Transfer (Cambridge, Mass.: The MIT Press, 1969), Chs. 6-8, indicates that the TU allocated the bulk of its resources (in both the Acquisition and the Dissemination Branches) to attempted specific item transfers.

4. See ADL, Space Technology Transfer and Developing Nations, prepared under NASA contract NASw-1649 (Washington, D.C.: CFSTI, October, 1968).

5. See ADL, Technology Transfer and Technology Utilization Program, report to the NASA OTU (Washington, D.C.: NASA, January, 1965), p. 9.

6. See NASA contract NSR 07-002-029, April, 1967; the exact value was $253,000 for a full year's operation.

7. See ADL, Technology Transfer and Technology Utilization Program, pp. 7-8. The ADL study carried out an experimental transfer program using a market-oriented, entrepreneurial approach and was able to transfer three NASA invention s to four companies and had several other transfers started when it was terminated after less than a year's operation and at a direct cost of $15,000 plus expenses.

8. See generally Edward Roberts, "Entrepreneurship and Technology," in Donald Marquis and William Gruber, eds., Factors in the Transfer of Technology (Cambridge, Mass.: The MIT Press, 1969),

pp. 219-37; and "Facts and Folklore in Research and Development Management," Industrial Management Review, VIII, 2 (Spring, 1967), 5-18, for a discussion of the transfer rates and mechanisms used by the spin-off company sample and of the small part externally generated technology plays in stimulating transfer.

9.   See Richard Rosenbloom and Francis Wolek, Technology, Information and Organization: Information Transfer in Industrial R&D, report prepared for NSF (Boston: Graduate School of Business Administration, Harvard University, June, 1967), Chs. 3 and 4; and Donald Marquis and Thomas Allen, "Communication Patterns in Applied Technology," American Psychologist, XXI (November, 1966), 1052-60, for the differences in scientist and engineer usage of externally developed technical information.

10.   See Ch. 3, section entitled "Process," for a discussion of the transfer process. See also Frank Lynn, An Investigation of the Rate of Development and Diffusion of Technology in Our Modern Industrial Society, report to the U.S. National Commission on Technology, Automation, and Economic Progress (Washington, D.C.: U.S. GPO, 1966); and Edwin Mansfield, Diffusion of Technological Change, "Reviews of Data on Research and Development," No. 31, NSF 61-52 (Washington, D.C.: U.S. GPO, October, 1961). See also Doctors, op. cit., Ch. 3, pp. 29-33.

11.   NPA, "Technology Transfer and Industrial Innovation," unpublished report prepared for NSF by Sumner Myers, et al. (Washington, D.C.: NSF, February, 1967). The study covered 567 "significant" innovations in three industries.

12.   See ARAC, op. cit., pp. 19-21. Renewal has been used as a single indicator of client satisfaction for ease of presentation, and expression of client satisfaction coincided very well with renewal.

13.   See NERAC, NASA Technology Utilization Project--Feasibility Study for Establishment of

Regional Dissemination Center for New England
(Springfield, Va.: CFSTI, April, 1967), pp. 82-94,
for a discussion of initial NERAC strategy of operation. Note particularly the emphasis on interpersonal transfer methods.

14. ARAC, op. cit., p. 5.

15. See NASA Contract NASr-175, Amendment No.
2 (with Wayne State University for calendar 1966)
and NASA Contract NSR 07-002-029 (with University
of Connecticut for April, 1967 to March 31, 1968).
From interviews with RDC personnel at four centers
it was clearly NASA policy to emphasize routinized
dissemination of technical information to larger industrial clients as a means to self-sufficiency.

16. See ADL, Technology Transfer and Technology Utilization Program.

17. See NPA, op. cit.; Roberts' "Entrepreneurship and Technology" and "Facts and Folklore . . .,";
and Daniel Shimshoni, "Aspects of Scientific Entrepreneurship," unpublished doctoral dissertation
(Kennedy School of Government, Harvard University,
May, 1966).

18. See, for example, Donald Schon, "Champions
for Radical New Inventions," Harvard Business Review,
XLI, 2 (March-April, 1963), 77-86; or Elting Morison,
"A Case of Innovation," Engineering and Science Monthly (April, 1950), 5-11.

19. See, for example, DRI, The Commercial Applications of Missile/Space Technology, NASA-sponsored
report (Springfield, Va.: CFSTI, June, 1963); or
NPA, op. cit.

20. NERAC, An Account of the Activities and
Results of the First Year of Operation of the New
England Research Application Center, prepared under
NASA Contract NSR 07-002-029 (Storrs, Conn.: NERAC,
March 31, 1968), pp. 26-27.

7

CONCLUSIONS
AND
RECOMMENDATIONS

NASA has devoted a great deal of time, effort, and money to promoting and measuring technology transfer from its R&D and related portions of the DOD and the AEC R&D programs to commercial industry. The bulk of this effort has been spent on assembling a vast semi-automated aerospace library and a few thousand reports of specific aerospace inventions, and on disseminating this aerospace literature collection and a few thousand specific invention reports to commercial industry. A number of mechanisms for publicity and dissemination have been used, including numerous articles, comments, and public relations releases in the trade and commercial presses. NASA has also sponsored a number of seminars and conferences on many areas of possible application. Finally, they established a network of RDC's to work directly with commercial industry.

The publicity portion of the program appears to have been successful in that the DRI survey of five industries indicated that more than 50 percent of the technologists sampled in those industries had heard of one or more types of NASA literature.[1] The dissemination portion has been less successful, since less than half of those hearing of the NASA

literature have made any use of it. Still, for an
organization just over ten years old and competing
for attention with many other sources of technical
literature, the publicity and dissemination program
appear to have achieved relatively widespread acquaintance among potential users. Also, judged be-
side the efforts of the other major science agencies that make available their R&D work product to
industry, NASA has done a commendable job of literature collection, publicity, and dissemination.

The real problem is how this vast program of
collection, publicity, and dissemination is related
to the stated agency objective of horizontal technology transfer. The agency has publicly distinguished between dissemination and transfer and has
said its intent is to promote measurable horizontal
transfer, not just dissemination. The RDC's have
been advertised as experimental transfer agents.
But, in practice, the NASA program has been geared
to dissemination, not transfer, and the RDC's have
become largely technical librarians or dissemination agents, providing searches of technical literature for industrial fee-paying clients.

NASA has sponsored a number of study and experimental projects theoretically aimed at understanding the transfer process. But, with the ex-
ception of a very few projects such as the modest
experimental transfer project at ADL and the much
more extensive research program at the MIT Sloan
School, the other study projects have been aimed
more at uncovering literature dissemination patterns than at increasing our understanding of the
transfer process.

Transfer is, of course, an extremely complex
process, particularly where it must occur largely
by analogy and organizational and institutional
lines must be crossed. Measures of horizontal
transfer have simply not been developed. Thus the
NASA program has not been very successful in ex-
tending our knowledge of transfer, but it has provided some useful information about technical information flow and usage.

Horizontal transfer requires that technical information be transferred from one person to another. However, the methodology of transfer is apparently quite different from that of literature dissemination, in that interpersonal contact on a continuing basis appears to be necessary to motivate the adoption of a new item of technology. It may be, however, that general area transfer can be motivated by less intensive interpersonal contact. Literature dissemination, conferences, and seminars may play a large part in general area transfer.

The present study has been directed at measuring the effectiveness of the NASA program as a mechanism for both specific item and general area transfer. It is usually much easier to place a value on specific item transfer and to compare this value with the cost of a program than it is to place a value on general area transfer. Indirect measures, such as willingness to pay for NASA technology or user expressions of value, are some indication of value. However, placing a monetary figure on the value of general area transfer remains quite difficult, particularly in view of the time required for payoff of the transfer process. Even specific item transfers are difficult to value, since short-term return on investment may in no way measure the long-term value of the transfer.

Nevertheless, with all these difficulties in valuing transfer, it is the conclusion of this study that the present NASA program has not generated transfer equal to its cost, either in terms of specific items or in the more general area. Nor has the program done what it might to use even its negative results to increase our understanding of the horizontal transfer process.

The NASA transfer program has cost between $4 and $10 million each year since 1962, and the measurable economic returns do not amount to a fraction of that expenditure. This is not to deny that considerable transfer of space/defense technology to commercial application has occurred during this period; it is simply that the NASA transfer program has not directly stimulated much of this transfer. The Myers and Roberts studies both found that a substantial amount of transfer had occurred during roughly the same period of time.[2] The Roberts spin-off company sample has even been experiencing an accelerating rate of transfer. Likewise, the Shimshoni study indicates that there has been a considerable amount of transfer in the scientific instrument industry.[3] Of course, all three studies cover limited segments of commercial industry and their time frames are somewhat different. Still, it does appear that considerable transfer is presently going on, but not primarily stimulated by literature dissemination. Although the availability of externally generated literature may play some part, the primary mechanisms appear to be continuing interpersonal contact with vendors, technical colleagues, and customers (for the Myers study), technical entrepreneurship, and technologist mobility (for the Roberts and Shimshoni samples).

NASA has been unable or unwilling to use the results of these studies to reshape its transfer program, nor has it taken advantage of the results of the ADL experimental program showing that NASA inventions could be sold to commercial industry through a market-oriented, interpersonal sales technique. An important question is whether a mission-oriented agency such as NASA can afford to support experimental programs which may cause it embarrassment at Congressional hearings. It has been less threatening for the agency to present document distribution statistics or Tech Brief production and distribution numbers than to support possibly controversial transfer experimentation and research.

The following are the specific conclusions and recommendations and unresolved questions of this study.

CONCLUSIONS

The first conclusion is that the NASA publicity and dissemination programs, taken as a whole, have not stimulated very much transfer, though they may have a long-term impact--if only in making commercial industry more aware of the sophisticated technology being produced under federal R&D contracts.

The second conclusion is that other mechanisms of transfer, such as technologist mobility, technical entrepreneurship, and continuing interpersonal contact, appear to have been superior for horizontal transfers.

Third, the RDC programs, specifically, have generated very little transfer, either specific item or general area. The RDC's are, however, generally perceived by industrial users as relatively fast, efficient technical librarians, and they do provide a useful dissemination function for technical literature.

Finally, NASA insistence on self-support within three to five years has largely precluded any experimentation or study of the transfer process by the RDC's. It has also acted to inhibit the establishment of effective feedback systems.

RECOMMENDATIONS

It is recommended that NASA alter its major focus from technical literature acquisition and dissemination to an experimental transfer program. To that end the following changes are suggested:

1. The RDC's should be given longer-term grants, rather than one year contracts. The time span of support should be commensurate with that of the transfer process, perhaps ten to fifteen years. (Special enabling legislation may be required.)

2. The RDC's should be encouraged to experiment with many different types of organizations-- universities, hospitals, non-profit research centers, industrial firms, and any others that appear

to offer fruitful opportunities to explore the
transfer process.

3.   The RDC's should structure all their experiments to ensure adequate feedback as a basis
for better understanding the transfer process.

4.   The RDC self-support requirement should be
dropped and fees obtained from clients should be
used as only a partial measure of interest in
space/defense technology, not as the sole measure
of RDC effectiveness.

5.   Other organizations, such as non-profit
research institutes and better quality universities,
should be involved in the program. Also, profit-
making organizations such as ADL should be used to
perform some of the more obviously applied transfer
experiments where their extensive knowledge of the
market for new technology could be effectively employed.

It is also recommended that other science
agencies participate in funding experimental transfer programs, in order to ensure their interest in
transfer and to provide participating organizations
some pluralism of funding sources.

Another recommendation is that a program similar to the Department of Commerce's former STS Program could provide an attractive vehicle for transfer experiments and for the establishment of long-
term, effective feedback mechanisms. However, the
intent of the STS enabling act was to focus on car-
rying out dissemination or transfer rather than on
increasing understanding of the process of providing information feedback for improvement. It is
recommended that the act be amended, if necessary,
to permit a much more experimental approach, including the funding of studies designed to explore
alternative approaches and to devise transfer experiments, and that the STS Program be reconstituted
to accomplish these objectives.

Finally, Congress should make it an explicit and important part of each technological agency's charter (present and future) to investigate ways of promoting transfer of its results to other sectors of the private economy and of the government. DOD particularly should be required to institute its own internal transfer program and should actively assist other agency programs, as it is indeed beginning to do in a few fields, such as housing.

It is unreasonable for federal agencies which use so large a proportion of this country's R&D resources for relatively narrow, mission-oriented programs not to devote some attention to enhancing the potential for secondary application of the results of their R&D programs. What is needed is a national policy which requires that each federal agency employing a substantial amount of R&D resources become involved in transfer activities. The initial aim of these activities should be to increase our understanding of the transfer process and to foster an attitude change within the major science and technology agencies that will give greater importance to transfer. Transfer should be viewed as an important part of each agency's mission, not a minor staff function or a propaganda device to sell its program.

THE NEED FOR FUTURE RESEARCH

This study has left unresolved a number of important questions concerning the transfer process that require further study and experimentation. These unresolved questions include the following:

1. What will be the long-term impact of the NASA TUP on horizontal transfer of space/defense technology and, more generally, on commercial industrial receptivity to sophisticated new technology? The findings of the present study indicate that the NASA program has in the short term promoted very little transfer and has created very

little receptivity among commercial firms for space/
defense technology. However, the program may have
a cumulative educational impact which will in the
long term enhance industrial receptivity to externally generated technology.

2. In particular, further study is needed to
determine whether the TUP is creating greater receptivity to externally generated technology among
management or other functional areas in commercial
firms.

3. The effect of the RDC program should be
studied at intervals over a long time period, such
as ten to twenty years, commensurate with the time
scale of technological diffusion. Such long-term
impact studies may provide valuable insights for
other federal programs.

4. If the DOA's Cooperative Extension Service
were measured on its short-term transfer effectiveness, how would it compare with the TUP? In particular, what has been the average time scale of
transfer in the agriculture sector, and what have
been the characteristics of these transfers? Has
there been much horizontal transfer, and what mechanisms of transfer have been used? To what extent
are the lessons of the agricultural transfer program
applicable to the industrial sector of the economy?

5. Other federal transfer programs, such as
the AEC's Industrial Cooperation Program and the
much older Department of Interior Office of Coal
Research Program, should be studied, since they
would provide transfer experience in a number of
other commercial industrial areas.

6. Additional study is needed to determine
whether the characteristics of technical entrepreneurs can be identified and a predictive model of
entrepreneurship constructed. Also to be studied
is the question of whether technical entrepreneurship can be fostered readily within existing organizations or whether the founding of spin-off firms

is inevitable and, moreover, is an optimum mechanism for fostering technical entrepreneurship.

7.   The spin-off studies of Roberts and his colleagues need to be extended to other geographical areas.   They should also be extended in time to determine whether the high rates of commercial diversification will continue.   More work is also needed to determine the effects of federal agency policy on the success or failure of these firms and what other environmental factors account for large numbers of spin-off firms in one area of the country and very few in other areas, despite large federal R&D expenditures in many areas.

8.   Better measures of horizontal transfer are needed, for both specific item and general area transfers.   A more complete conceptual framework of transfer which will allow for some prediction of transfer and for meaningful experimental programs is desirable.

9.   A detailed study of the effects of federal agency overhead R&D funding on innovation is needed. The effects on transfer of agency policies allowing contractors to keep the results of this overhead R&D work proprietary should be investigated and implications of alternative policies should be explored.

10.   How can transfer be fostered in the public sector and, in particular, what mechanisms are needed to motivate transfer between the space/ defense agencies and agencies such as the Department of Health, Education and Welfare or the Department of Transportation?   Also, what can be done to motivate transfer between federal, state, and local governmental agencies?

11.   How do federal policies concerning contractor rights to intellectual property affect transfer?   More specifically, what effect have present agency policies had on the production and use of patents and trade secrets by contractors?

Are there alternative policies more conducive to the production and transfer of specific items of space/defense technology?

12. Has the reluctance of federal agencies to grant exclusive licenses affected third party utilization of government-owned patents?

13. The study by Richard Carpenter, Policy Planning for Technology Transfer, suggested that the NASA New Technology Reporting Clause be extended to other federal agency contracts. Would such a requirement spur more contract reporting? If so, would it hinder the primary mission of these agencies by discouraging private firm participation in government R&D?

14. Some commentators have suggested that federal R&D is becoming more and more esoteric, and thus transfer is becoming more and more difficult. Is this assertion justified? How does one measure the relative level of sophistication of government R&D, and whether this sophistication is changing and at what rate?

15. Can mechanisms be established to minimize agency reluctance to sponsor meaningful transfer experiments and studies in their area of technology?

16. How should the cost effectiveness of transfer studies and experiments be measured? Can any short-term justification be offered for a significant investment in technology transfer programs?

17. DOD's policies largely shape the environment of any transfer program. What can be done to motivate DOD interest in long-term transfer programs?

FINAL REMARKS

The weighty list of recommendations might indicate to the reader a hopeless morass of problems

in the area of technology transfer. Many of the
problems identified in this volume can be attributed
to the inherent dysfunction of a bureaucratic organization such as NASA. Other problems related to
research that is not properly designed or focused.
Hopefully, a major value of this book will be to
direct future study of the process of technology
transfer. Using a clearly defined and structured
approach, it may be possible to enhance the transfer of government-sponsored R&D to the commercial
sector of our economy.

NOTES

1. DRI, Channels of Technology Acquisition in
Commercial Firms and the NASA Dissemination Program
(Springfield, Va.: CFSTI, June, 1967), p. 47.

2. See Edward Roberts, "Entrepreneurship and
Technology," in Donald Marquis and William Gruber,
eds., Factors in the Transfer of Technology (Cambridge, Mass.: The MIT Press, 1969), pp. 219-37;
and NPA, "Technology Transfer and Industrial Innovation," unpublished report prepared for NSF by
Sumner Myers, et al. (Washington, D.C.: NSF,
February, 1967).

3. Daniel Shimshoni, "Aspects of Scientific
Entrepreneurship," unpublished doctoral dissertation (Kennedy School of Government, Harvard University, June, 1966).

APPENDIXES

NERAC CLIENT COMPANIES

The list was supplied by NERAC and by NASA TUP, and was complete as of January 1, 1969.

Specified here is the division or corporate unit contacted, but some data were collected on overall corporate characteristics. However, these data are not deemed significant for analyzing transfer of space/defense technology to the establishment contacted except as noted in the text.

Companies marked with * were contacted by telephone and mail questionnaire. Companies marked with ** were contacted by mail questionnaire only. Only one of the four companies contacted solely by mail sent any response. Companies marked with *** could not be located in standard industrial directories and therefore were not contacted. All the other forty-four NERAC clients were contacted in person and participated in on-site discussions of their transfer activities.

Alberox Corporation
New Bedford, Mass.

American Chemical and
  Refining Co., Inc.
Waterbury, Conn.

Associated Spring
  Corporation*
Bristol, Conn.

BLH Electronics
Waltham, Mass.

Beta Instruments Co., Inc.
Newton, Mass.

Buff and Buff Manufac-
  turing Co.
Boston, Mass.

Clairol, Inc.
Research Laboratory
Stamford, Conn.

Conversion Chemical
  Corporation
Rockville, Conn.

Cyanamid Company*
Plastics of Polymers
  Department
Stamford, Conn.

Dynamics Corporation
  of America**
East Hartford, Conn.

Dynamics Research
  Corporation
Stoneham, Mass.

EG&G
Bedford, Mass.

General Electric
Direct Energy Conver-
  sion Project
Lynn, Mass.

General Latex and
  Chemical Corporation
Research Center
North Billerica, Mass.

Greenfield Components
  Corporation
Greenfield, Mass.

Greenfield Tap and Die
Greenfield, Mass.
(Now division of TRW;
  in 1967, division of
  United Greenfield)

Harris Manufacturing
  Company
Cambridge, Mass.

Heald Corporation
Worcester, Mass.
(division of Cincinnati
  Milling)

H. G. Ives Company*
New Haven, Conn.

The Ingraham Company**
Bristol, Conn.

Honeywell
Computer Control Di-
  vision
Framingham, Mass.

Jet Vac Corporation
Waltham, Mass.

Jones and Lamson**
(division of Textron)

Kellems Company, Inc.**
Stoningham, Conn.

Lincoln Laboratories (MIT)
Lexington, Mass.

Arthur D. Little, Inc.
Cambridge, Mass.

Logan Electronics, Inc.
Revere, Mass.

Lowell Corporation
Worcester, Mass.

Microsonics, Inc.
Weymouth, Mass.
(division of Sangamo
   Electric Co.)

Millers Falls Company
Millers Falls, Mass.
(division of Ingersoll-
   Rand)

Monsanto
Polymers and Hydro-
   carbons Division
Springfield, Mass.

Morse Twist Drill and
   Machine Company
New Bedford, Mass.
(Gulf and Western
   subsidiary)

Norton Company
Worcester, Mass.

Pickard and Burns
   Electronics
Waltham, Mass.
(division of LTV)

Polaroid Corporation
Cambridge, Mass.

Presmet Corporation
Worcester, Mass.

Quantum, Inc.
Wallingford, Conn.

RCA
Memory Products Division
Needham, Mass.

Raymond Engineering, Inc.
Middletown, Conn.

Raytheon Corporation
Corporate Staff
Lexington, Mass.

Rice Barton Corporation
Worcester, Mass.

Roux Laboratories,
   Inc.***
New York, N.Y.

Spectrum Systems, Inc.*
Waltham, Mass.

TRG, Inc.
Boston, Mass.
(division of Control
   data Corporation)

Technical Resources, Inc.
Waltham, Mass.

Teradyne, Inc.
Boston, Mass.

Thermo-Electron
   Corporation
Waltham, Mass.

The Henry G. Thompson
  Company
New Haven, Conn.
(division of Vermont
  America Corporation)

United Carr, Inc.
Research Laboratory
Watertown, Mass.

United Shoe Machinery
  Corporation
Central Research
  Division
Beverly, Mass.

Van Dyck Corporation***
Southport, Conn.

Worcester Valve Company, Inc.
Worcester, Mass.

Worthington Control Company
Norwood, Mass.
(division of Studebaker-
  Worthington Corporation

Xenon Corporation
Watertown, Mass.

ARAC CLIENT COMPANIES

Companies Included in Survey

Abbott Laboratories
North Chicago, Ill.

Ball Brothers Service
  Corporation
Muncie, Ind.

Borg-Warner
Research Center
Des Plaines, Illinois

Brookside Corporation
McCordsville, Ind.

Chase Brass and
  Copper
Solon, Ohio

Dubois Chemicals
Cincinnati, O.

Esterline Angus Company
  Indianapolis, Ind.

General Electric Company
Motor and Generator Division
Erie, Pa.

General Motors Corporation
Delco-Radio Division
Kokomo, Ind.

General Motors Corporation
Delco-Remy Division
Engineering Center
Anderson, Ind.

B. F. Goodrich Company
Research Center
Brecksville, O.

Harris Intertype
Cleveland, Ohio

Hobart Brothers Company
Troy, O.

ITT-Federal Laboratories
Fort Wayne, Ind.

James Electronics, Inc.
Chicago, Ill.

Jenn Air Products
   Corporation
Indianapolis, Ind.

Kerr-McGee Oil
   Industries, Inc.
Oklahoma City, Okla.

Keystone Consolidated
National Lock Division
Rockford, Ill.

Eli Lilly, Inc.
Indianapolis, Ind.

New Castle Products, Inc.
New Castle, Ind.

Penn Controls, Inc.
Goshen, Ind.

Pullman Standard
Chicago, Ill.

Roberts Brass Manufac-
   turing Company*
Mitchell, Ind.
(division of United States
   Brass Corporation)

All ARAC Clients Contacted

This list represents sixty of ninety-three
client companies of ARAC as of January 1, 1969. It
was not possible to contact the other thirty-three
companies from the data supplied by the NASA TUP,
and they declined to furnish additional data. Companies marked with * responded but supplied no
usable data; those marked with ** returned completed questionnaires or supplied data; all others did
not respond by March 15, 1969.

Abbott Corporation**

American Machine and
   Foundry Company

Arvin Industries, Inc.

Ashland Oil Refining
   Company

Ball Brothers Company

Bardons and Oliver, Inc.

Borg-Warner**

Brookside Corporation**

The Carborundum Company

Chase Brass and Copper
   Company

Cincinnati Milling
   Machine Company

Clark Equipment Company

Collins Radio Company

Cummins Engine
  Company, Inc.

Dubois Chemicals**

Esterline-Angus
  Instruments
  Company, Inc.**

Firestone Tire and
  Rubber Company*

Franklin Electric
  Company

General Electric
  Company**

General Motors
  Corporation:
  Delco-Remy Division**
  Delco-Radio Division**

B. F. Goodrich Company**

Goodman Manufacturing
  Company, Streeter Amet
  Division

Harris Intertype**

Harshaw Chemical Company*

Hobart Brothers Company**

Hoffman Specialty Manu-
  facturing Corporation*

Indiana Instrument and
  Chemical Corporation

ITT-Federal Laboratories**

James Electronics, Inc.**

Jenn Air Products
  Corporation**

Josten's, Inc.

KDI Corporation

Kerr-McGee Oil
  Industries, Inc.**

Keystone Consolidated,
  Division of National
  Lock**

Kursh-Kash, Inc.

Eli Lilly, Inc.**

Mead Johnson Company

Monsanto Company*

National Cash Register
  Company

New Castle Products,
  Inc.**

Nibco, Inc.

Nooter Corporation

Nuclear Chicago Corpo-
  ration

Owens-Illinois, Inc.

Penn Controls, Inc.**

Pullman Standard**

Roberts Brass Manufac-
turing Company**

Rohr Corporation

Sakes-Tarzian, Inc.

Howard W. Sams, Inc.*

Skelly Oil Company

The Steelcraft Manu-
facturing Company

Sun Oil Company

Unitrode Corporation*

Universal Oil Company

Vulcan Materials Company*

Welco Industries, Inc.

Westinghouse Electric
Corporation

Xerox Corporation

RDC CLIENT GUIDE/QUESTIONNAIRE

I. Types of information disseminated by the following (please check all appropriate items)

   A. NASA Specific Invention Reports
      (Tech Briefs)   _____

   B. Other NASA technology reports   _____

   C. Computerized searches of NASA tapes   _____

       1. Narrow-interest profiles   _____
       2. Broad-brush surveys   _____
       3. Retrospective (one-shot) surveys _____
       4. Continuing interest profiles   _____

   D. Computerized searches of other
      government agencies or other
      organization tapes   _____
      (please specify which agencies
      or organizations)

      _____

      _____

      _____

E.   RDC consultants--application en-
     gineering or other personalized
     technical assistance   _____

F.   Special services, such as procurement of
     Tech Brief follow-up materials, govern-
     ment agency bid-proposal data, referral
     assistance, etc. (please specify)

     _____

     _____

     _____

G.   Please indicate the relative usefulness of
     the different information sources pro-
     vided by RDC

     _____

     _____

     _____

II. Persons receiving and using RDC-supplied
     information (please check all
     recipients and users)

     A.   Top management   _____

     B.   Functional management   _____

          1. R&D   _____
          2. Marketing   _____
          3. Production   _____
          4. Other   _____

     C.   Line or staff personnel not part
          of management

          1. Research laboratories   _____
              a. Engineers   _____
              b. Scientists   _____

        2. Production   _____
           a. Engineering   _____
           b. Quality control or
              reliability   _____

        3. Marketing   _____
           a. Forecast group   _____
           b. Product improvement _____

D. Other (please specify)

_____

_____

_____

E. Please indicate which groups find the
    NERAC information most useful

_____

_____

_____

III. Uses for information (please check all appro-
    priate categories)

A. Planning   _____

    1. New product(s)   _____
    2. Tool in present project planning _____
    3. Scouting competition--state-
       of-the-art survey   _____

B. Diversification evaluation   _____

C. Background information   _____

    1. Preparation or evaluation of
       a proposal   _____
    2. Investigation of a technical
       or scientific problem   _____
    3. Preparation of technical reports _____

    D. General stimulus   _____

    E. Other (please specify) _____

       _____

    F. Please indicate which categories form the greatest areas of use

       _____

       _____

IV. Actual or planned technology transfer occurring as a result of RDC information

    A. Type(s) of technology transferred from NERAC and origin (government, international, journal article, other)

       _____

       _____

    B. Type of transfer mechanism

       1. Mail or telephone   _____
       2. Interpersonal contact   _____

    C. Magnitude of investment required (estimate)   _____

    D. State the degree of importance you attached to obtaining legal rights to the transfer item(s)

       _____

       _____

    E. Time required to bring to point of marketable end item or to use in present production process   _____

F. Profit or quality improvement expected

_____

V. Actual or planned technology transfer occur-
    ring as a result of other space/defense tech-
    nical information commonly employed

    A. Type(s) of technology transferred from
        sources other than RDC and origin (gov-
        ernment, international, journal article,
        other)

        _____

        _____

    B. Type of transfer mechanism

        _____

        _____

    C. Magnitude of investment required   _____

    D. Time required to bring to point of
        marketable end item use or to use
        in present production process   _____

    E. Profit or quality improvement expected

        _____

        _____

VI. Cost of services supplied by RDC

    A. Monetary (yearly)   _____

    B. Evaluation and intra-firm dissemination
        cost (man-hours yearly)

        _____

VII.   How satisfied are clients with services and
       information received?

_____

_____

_____

_____

VIII. User characteristics. If the user is a divi-
       sion or a subsidiary of a larger corpora-
       tion, please answer the following questions
       for the division or subsidiary and send a
       copy of the latest available annual report
       with this questionnaire

       A. Corporate size

           1. Employees   _____
           2. Sales   _____
           3. Average growth rate in sales
               in last three years   _____
           4. Number of degreed technical
               personnel employed   _____
           5. Number of degreed technical
               personnel employed in R&D
               Ph.D.'s ___   M.S.'s ___   Other ___
           6. Non-NERAC sources of space/defense
               technical information commonly
               employed

               _____

               _____

           7. Other types of technical information
               sources commonly employed

               _____

               _____

               _____

8. Major product line(s) and services

_____

_____

_____

9. Major type of customers (i.e., con-
    sumers, government agencies, other
    industries)

_____

_____

10. R&D performed as a percent
     of sales   _____

11. Total annual percent of sales
     under R&D contract to
     (a) government agency (ies)   _____

12. Total percentage of sales to
     the government   _____

IX. Comments. Please take this opportunity to
     make any other comments that would be use-
     ful for this research project. Be assured
     that all answers will be kept strictly con-
     fidential and only used as part of statis-
     tical averages or disguised case reports.
     Thanks so much.

Please PRINT the following information:

Company Name   _____
Division or Subsidiary Name   _____
Location (City, State)   _____
Name   _____
Title   _____

QUESTIONNAIRE FOR SELECTED
CORPORATE TECHNOLOGISTS

(All users of RDC information, not just technologists, were asked to complete this questionnaire
at companies interviewed. This same form was used
for ARAC and NERAC users, only the RDC name was
changed.)

1. How did you learn of the RDC project?
    a. RDC publicity   _____
    b. RDC personal presentation   _____
    c. Newsletter   _____
    d. Public agency or media   _____
    e. Other (please specify) _____
        _____
        _____

2. How did you expect to use the information?
    a. To solve a specific technical
            problem   _____
    b. To solve a specific socio-
            technical problem   _____
    c. For background information on a
            potential area of interest   _____
    d. To find out who had done work in
            the area of interest   _____
    e. For proposal preparation   _____
    f. To find out what had been done by
            others in the area of interest   _____
    g. Other (please specify) _____
        _____
        _____

3. For what purpose(s) did you actually use the
    information?
    a. To solve a specific technical
            problem   _____
    b. To solve a specific socio-
            technical problem   _____
    c. For background information on a
            potential area of interest   _____
    d. To find out who had done work in
            the area of interest   _____

    e. For proposal preparation   _____
    f. To find out what had been done by
        others in the area of interest   _____
    g. Other (please specify) _____

        _____

        _____

4. Was the information useful for the specific
    purpose intended?   Yes _____   No _____

5. Was the information useful for related pur-
    pose(s), not intended prior to the search?
    Yes _____   No _____

6. Was the response time of the information
    important?   Yes _____   No _____

7. Was the response time: Excellent _____
    Good _____   Fair _____   Poor _____

8. Which information or service was most useful?
    (Please rank in order of usefulness.)
    Computer printout _____ Abstracts _____
    RDC-supplied documents _____ References con-
    tained in the documents _____ Other RDC
    services (please specify) _____

    _____

9. Did useful information come from area(s) of
    technology not the same as the problem area?
    Yes _____   No _____
    If Yes, please specify how different areas
    of technology were useful _____

    _____

10. Was information from non-governmental sources
     supplied by RDC?   Yes _____   No _____

11. What were the non-governmental sources?
     (please specify) _____

     _____

     _____

12.   Please rank all information sources supplied
      by RDC according to usefulness.

      _____   ____

      _____   ____

      _____   ____

      _____   ____

      _____   ____

13.   Were any specific inventions or new areas of
      application found as a result of RDC-supplied
      information or service? Yes _____ No _____
      If Yes, please specify _____

      _____

      _____

14.   What dollar value would you place on the RDC
      information alone? $ _____   Cost $ _____

15.   What value would you place on other
      RDC services? $ _____

16.   Please list non-RDC sources of space/defense
      technology employed

      _____

      _____

      _____

17.   How would you compare the value of these other
      information sources with ARAC? Please be as
      specific as possible. _____

      _____

      _____

18. Please take the remaining space on this ques-
    tionnaire to make any comments that would
    prove helpful for this research project.
    Please be assured that any comments made
    here or elsewhere on this questionnaire will
    be kept in strictest confidence. Thanks so
    much.

NAME (please print)

TITLE

COMPANY & DIVISION

SELECTED BIBLIOGRAPHY

BOOKS

Bauer, Raymond, and Kenneth Gergen, eds. The Study
     of Policy Formation. New York: The Free
     Press, 1968.

Blood, Jerome, ed. Utilizing R&D By-Products. New
     York: American Management Association, 1967.

Bright, James. Research, Development and Techno-
     logical Innovation. Homewood, Illinois:
     Richard D. Irwin, 1964.

Brooks, Harvey. The Government of Science. Cam-
     bridge, Massachusetts: The MIT Press, 1968.

Coleman, James, Elihu Katz, and Herbert Menzel.
     Medical Innovation: A Diffusion Study.
     Indianapolis: Bobbs-Merrill, 1966.

Danhof, Clarence. Government Contracting and Tech-
     nological Change. Washington, D.C.: The
     Brookings Institution, 1968.

Doctors, Samuel. The Management of Technological
     Change. New York: American Management Asso-
     ciation, 1970.

_____. The Role of the Federal Agencies in Tech-
     nology Transfer. Cambridge, Massachusetts:
     The MIT Press, 1969.

Drucker, Peter. The Age of Discontinuity. New
     York: Harper & Row, 1968.

Dupré, Stefen, and Sanford Lakoff. Science and the
     Nation. Englewood Cliffs, New Jersey:
     Prentice-Hall, 1962.

Enos, John. Petroleum Progress and Profits: A
     History of Process Innovation. Cambridge,
     Massachusetts: The MIT Press, 1962.

Galbraith, John. The New Industrial State. New
     York: The New American Library, 1967.

Hamberg, Daniel. R&D Essays on the Economics of Research and Development. New York: Random House, 1963.

Jewkes, John, David Sawers, and Richard Stillerman. The Sources of Invention. New York: St. Martin's Press, 1961.

Machlup, Fritz. The Production and Distribution of Knowledge in the United States. Princeton: Princeton University Press, 1962.

Mansfield, Edwin. The Economics of Technological Change. New York: W. W. Norton, 1968.

March, James, and Herbert Simon. Organizations. New York: John Wiley & Sons, 1967.

Marquis, Donald, and William Gruber, eds. Factors in the Transfer of Technology. Cambridge, Massachusetts: The MIT Press, 1969.

Morison, Elting E. Men, Machines, and Modern Times. Cambridge, Massachusetts: The MIT Press, 1966.

Mullis, E., ed. Report of the National Conference on Technology Utilization and Economic Growth. Bloomington, Indiana: Aerospace Research Applications Center, August, 1967.

National Bureau of Economic Research. The Rate and Direction of Inventive Activity: Economic and Social Factors. Princeton: Princeton University Press, 1962.

Nelson, Richard, Merton Peck, and Edward Kalachek. Technology, Economic Growth, and Public Policy. Washington, D.C.: The Brookings Institution, 1967.

Peck, Merton, and Frederick Scherer. The Weapons Acquisition Process: An Economic Analysis. Boston: Division of Research, Graduate School of Business Administration, Harvard University, 1962.

Price, Don K. The Scientific Estate. Cambridge,
    Massachusetts: Harvard University Press, 1965.

Rodgers, Everett. Diffusion of Innovation. New
    York: The Free Press of Glencoe, 1962.

Scherer, Frederick. The Weapons Acquisition Process:
    Economic Incentives. Boston: Division of Re-
    search, Graduate School of Business Administra-
    tion, Harvard University, 1964.

Schmookler, Jacob. Invention and Economic Growth.
    Cambridge, Massachusetts: Harvard University
    Press, 1966.

Schon, Donald. Technology and Change. New York:
    Delacorte Press, 1967.

            PUBLISHED ARTICLES AND REPORTS

Aerospace Industries Association of America, Inc.
    Application of Aerospace Technology and Systems
    Techniques in Civil Areas. Washington, D.C.:
    AIAA, May, 1967.

American Chemical Service. CAS Today: Facts and
    Figures About Chemical Abstracts Service.
    Columbus, Ohio: Chemical Abstracts Service,
    1967.

Bauer, Raymond. "The Obstinate Audience: The In-
    fluence Process from the Point of View of
    Social Communication," American Psychologist,
    XIX, 5 (May, 1964), 319-28.

_____. "Problems in Review: Executives Probe
    Space," Harvard Business Review, XXXVIII, 5
    (September-October, 1960), 6-15.

Comanor, William. "Market Structure, Product Dif-
    ferentiation and Industrial Research," The
    Quarterly Journal of Economics, LXXXI (Novem-
    ber, 1967), 639-57.

Danhof, Clarence. Technology Transfer by People Transfer. Washington, D.C.: Program of Policy Studies in Science and Technology, The George Washington University Press, August, 1969.

Freeman, Christopher. "Research and Development in Electronic Capital Goods," National Institute Economic Review (November, 1965), 40-91.

Furash, Edward. "Businessmen Review the Space Effort," Harvard Business Review, XLI (September-October, 1963), 14-48.

Gilmore, John, and Dean Coddington. "Diversification Guides for Defense Firms," Harvard Business Review, XLIV, 3 (May-June, 1966), 144-59.

Haggerty, James. "The Giant Harvest from Space--Today and Tomorrow," Air Force and Space Digest (February, 1970), 30-43.

Havelock, Ronald G., et al. Planning for Innovation Through Dissemination and Utilization of Knowledge. Ann Arbor, Michigan: Institute for Social Research, Center for Research on Utilization of Scientific Knowledge, July, 1969.

Herner, Saul, and Mary Herner. "Information Needs and Uses in Science and Technology." Annual Review of Information Science and Technology. Edited by Carlos Cuadra. American Documentation Institute, "Annual Review Series," Vol. II. New York: Interscience Publishers, 1967. Pp. 1-33.

Holman, Mary. "Government Research and Development Inventions--A New Resource?," Land Economics, XLI (August, 1965), 231-38.

Holst, Helge. "Government Patent Policy--Its Impact on Contractor Cooperation with the Government and Widespread Use of Government Sponsored Technology," Patent, Trademark, and Copyright Journal of Research and Education, IX, 2 (Summer, 1965), 273-96.

Howick, George, et al. "R&D Inputs from Space Technology," Research/Development, XVII, 9 (September, 1966), 18-46.

Institute for Scientific Information. Services for
Efficient Retrieval and Dissemination of Scientific Information. Philadelphia: ISI, 1967.

Katz, Elihu, Martin Levin, and Herbert Hamilton.
"Traditions of Research on the Diffusion of
Innovation," American Sociological Review,
XXVIII (April, 1963), 237-52.

Kotel, Janet. "Bringing NASA's Fallout Down to
Earth," Mechanical Engineering (October, 1970),
18-23.

Marquis, Donald. Research Program on the Management
of Science and Technology. Cambridge, Massachusetts: The MIT Sloan School, 1968. Report
for 1966-67.

Marquis, Donald, and Thomas Allen. "Communication
Patterns in Applied Technology," American Psychologist, XXI (November, 1966), 1052-60.

Menzel, Herbert. "Information Needs and Uses in
Science and Technology." Annual Review of In-
formation Science and Technology. Edited by
Carlos Cuadra. American Documentation Insti-
tute, "Annual Review Series," Vol. I. New
York: Interscience Publishers, 1966. Pp. 41-69.

_____. "Scientific Communication: Five Themes from
Social Science Research," American Psychologist,
XXI (November, 1966), 999-1004.

Morison, Elting. "A Case Study of Innovation," Engineering and Science Monthly (April, 1950),
5-11.

Mossinghoff, Gerald, and Robert Allnutt. "Patent
Infringement in Government Procurement: A
Remedy Without a Right?," Notre Dame Law Re-
view, XLII (October, 1966), 5-28.

"NASA Cuts Back Spin-off Program," Electronics
    (September 30, 1968), 63.

Roberts, Edward. "Facts and Folklore in Research
    and Development Management," Industrial Manage-
    ment Review, VIII, 2 (Spring, 1967), 5-18.

Rosenbloom, Richard. Technology Transfer--Process
    and Policy: An Analysis of the Utilization of
    Technological By-Products of Military and Space
    R&D. Special Report No. 62. Washington, D.C.:
    National Planning Association, July, 1965.

_____. "The Transfer of Military Technology to
    Civilian Use." Technology in Western Civili-
    zation. Edited by Melvin Kranzberg and Carroll
    Pursell. Vol. II. New York: Oxford Univer-
    sity Press, 1967. Pp. 601-12.

Rosenbloom, Richard, and Francis Wolek. Technology,
    Information and Organization: Information
    Transfer in Industrial R&D. Report prepared
    for NSF. Boston: Graduate School of Business
    Administration, Harvard University, June, 1967.

Ryan, Bryce. "A Study in Technological Diffusion,"
    Rural Sociology, XIII (September, 1948), 273-85.

Sanders, Berkev. "Comparative Patent Yield from
    Government Versus Industry Financed R&D,"
    Patent, Trademark, and Copyright Journal of
    Research and Education, IX, 1 (Spring, 1965),
    1-24.

_____. "Patterns of Commercial Exploitation of
    Patented Inventions by Large and Small Com-
    panies," Patent, Trademark, and Copyright
    Journal of Research and Education, VIII, 1
    (Spring, 1964), 51-93.

Schon, Donald. "Champions for Radical New Inven-
    tions," Harvard Business Review, XLI, 2 (March-
    April, 1963), 77-86.

_____. "Innovation by Invasion," International Science and Technology, 27 (March, 1964), 52-60.

Schrage, Harry. "The R&D Entrepreneur: Profile of Success," Harvard Business Review, XLIII, 6 (November-December, 1965), 56-69.

Smith, William, and Daniel Creamer. R&D and Small Company Growth. New York: National Industrial Conference Board, 1968.

Solo, Robert. "Gearing Military R&D to Economic Growth," Harvard Business Review, XL, 6 (November-December, 1962), 49-60.

"Tune in to NASA's Technology-Transfer Program with Profit!" Plastics World (December, 1970).

Watson, Donald, Harold Bright, and Arthur Burns. "Federal Patent Policy in Contracts for Research and Development," Patent, Trademark, and Copyright Journal of Research and Education, IV, 4 (Winter, 1960), 299-434.

Welles, John, and Robert Waterman. "Space Technology: Pay-Off from Spin-Off," Harvard Business Review, XLII (July-August, 1964), 106-18.

PUBLIC DOCUMENTS

Allen, Thomas. Managing the Flow of Scientific and Technological Information. Final report to the Office of Science Information, National Science Foundation. Springfield, Virginia: Clearinghouse for Federal Scientific and Technical Information, September, 1966.

Aerospace Research Applications Center, University of Indiana. ARAC Operating Manual. Bloomington, Indiana: ARAC, July, 1964.

_____. Final Report, A Study of Information/Technology Transfer in Industrial Firms. Report prepared under NASA contract NSR 15-003-005. Bloomington, Indiana: ARAC, January 15, 1968.

_____. Final Five Year Report, Experiment to Transfer Technology from a University-Based Center. Report prepared under NASA contract SC-NASr-162. Bloomington, Indiana: ARAC, February, 1968.

_____. ARAC Technology Transfers. Prepared by C. Mullis. Bloomington, Indiana: ARAC, May, 1968.

_____. 1969 ARAC Services Catalog. Bloomington, Indiana: ARAC, January 1, 1969.

Center for the Application of Sciences and Technology, Wayne State University. From Aerospace Generated Technology Through University Research Facilities to Productive Application. Detroit: CAST, 1966.

Denver Research Institute. The Commercial Applications of Missile/Space Technology. NASA-sponsored report. Springfield, Virginia: Clearinghouse for Federal Scientific and Technical Information, September, 1963.

_____. Channels of Technology Acquisition in Commercial Firms and the NASA Dissemination Program. NASA-sponsored report. Springfield, Virginia: Clearinghouse for Federal Scientific and Technical Information, June, 1967.

_____. Project for the Analysis of Technology Transfer. Quarterly evaluation report No. 1. NASA-sponsored. Denver: DRI, June 15, 1968.

_____. Project for the Analysis of Technology Transfer. Quarterly evaluation report No. 2. NASA-sponsored. Denver: DRI, July 15, 1968.

_____. Project for the Analysis of Technology Trans-
fer. Quarterly evaluation report No. 3. NASA-
sponsored. Denver: DRI, October 18, 1968.

_____. Project for the Analysis of Technology Trans-
fer. Quarterly evaluation final report. NASA-
sponsored. Denver: DRI, November 13, 1968.

_____. Project for the Analysis of Technology Trans-
fer. Quarterly evaluation report No. 8. NASA-
sponsored. Denver: DRI, January 30, 1970.

_____. Project for the Analysis of Technology Trans-
fer. Annual report. NASA-sponsored. Denver:
DRI, March, 1970.

_____. Project for the Analysis of Technology Trans-
fer. Quarterly report No. 2. NASA-sponsored.
Denver: DRI, June 30, 1970.

Estle, Edwin. A Summary of the New England Economy:
Past, Present and Future. Report prepared for
the Federal Reserve Bank of Boston. Boston:
Federal Reserve Bank of Boston, August, 1966.

Federal Reserve Bank of Boston. New England Economic Almanac. Boston: Federal Reserve Bank
of Boston, 1966.

Harbridge House, Inc. Government Patent Policy
Study. Report prepared for Federal Council on
Science and Technology, Committee on Govern-
ment Patent Policy. Volumes I-IV. Washington,
D.C.: U.S. Government Printing Office, May 17,
1968.

The Illinois Institute of Technology Research Institute. Technology in Retrospect and Critical
Events in Science. Report prepared for National
Science Foundation. Chicago: IIT Research Institute, December 15, 1968.

The Knowledge Availability Systems Center, University of Pittsburgh. The Space and Technology
Transfer Program. Report prepared for NASA,
fourth annual report. Pittsburgh: KASC, June,
1968.

_____. KASC Information Services. Final report
for NASA. Pittsburgh: KASC, July, 1970.

Lesher, Richard, and George Howick. Assessing Technology Transfer. NASA Sp-5067. Washington,
D.C.: U.S. Government Printing Office, 1966.

Little, Arthur D., Inc. Projective Economic Studies
of New England. Report prepared for U.S. Army
Corps of Engineers. Cambridge, Massachusetts:
ADL, October 13, 1964.

_____. Technology Transfer and Technology Utiliza-
tion Program. Report to the NASA OTU. Washington, D.C.: NASA, January, 1965.

_____. Technology Transfer and Technology Utiliza-
tion Program. Report to the NASA OTU. Washington, D.C.: NASA, April, 1966.

_____. Transfer of Aerospace Technology in the
United States--A Critical Review. Report to
the Subcommittee of Enquiry into the Aircraft
Industry, United Kingdom. Cambridge, Massachusetts: ADL, July, 1966.

_____. Space Technology Transfer and Developing Na-
tions. Prepared for NASA. Springfield, Virginia: Clearinghouse for Scientific and Technical Information, 1968.

Lynn, Frank. An Investigation of the Rate of Development and Diffusion of Technology in Our Modern
Industrial Society. Report to the U.S. National
Commission on Technology, Automation and Economic Progress. Washington, D.C.: U.S. Government Printing Office, 1966.

Midwest Research Institute. Regional Dissemination
     Center Operation. Quarterly progress report.
     Prepared for NASA OTU. Kansas City, Missouri:
     MRI, July 14, 1967.

Myers, Sumner, and Donald Marquis. Successful In-
     dustrial Innovations. NSF 69-17. Washington,
     D.C.: U.S. Government Printing Office, May,
     1969.

National Academy of Sciences and National Academy of
     Engineering. Scientific and Technical Communi-
     cation. Washington, D.C.: National Academy of
     Sciences, 1969.

National Planning Association. "Technology Transfer
     and Industrial Innovation." Unpublished report
     prepared for National Science Foundation by
     Sumner Myers, et al. Washington, D.C.: Na-
     tional Science Foundation, February, 1967.

A National Program of Research for Agriculture.
     Sponsored jointly by the Association of State
     Universities and Land Grant Colleges and the
     U.S. Department of Agriculture. Washington,
     D.C.: U.S. Department of Agriculture, October,
     1966.

National Science Foundation. Industrial R&D Funds
     in Relation to Other Economic Variables. NSF
     64-25. Washington, D.C.: U.S. Government
     Printing Office, October, 1964.

_____. Technology Transfer and Innovation, 1966.
     NSF 67-5. Washington, D.C.: U.S. Government
     Printing Office, May, 1966.

_____. Federal Funds for Research, Development,
     and Other Scientific Activities: Fiscal Years
     1968, 1969, and 1970. NSF 69-31. Washington,
     D.C.: U.S. Government Printing Office, August,
     1969.

_____. Basic Research, Applied Research and Devel-
opment in Industry, 1965. NSF 67012. Washington, D.C.: U.S. Government Printing Office,
June, 1967.

_____. Research and Development in Industry, 1967.
NSF 69-28. Washington, D.C.: U.S. Government
Printing Office, July, 1969.

New England Research Application Center. NASA Technology Utilization Project--Feasibility Study
for Establishment of Regional Dissemination
Center for New England. Springfield, Virginia:
Clearinghouse for Federal Scientific and Technical Information, April, 1967.

_____. Quarterly Progress Report. NASA Contract
NSR 07-002-029. Washington, D.C.: NASA OTU,
November, 1967.

_____. An Account of the Activities and Results of
the First Year of Operation of the New England
Research Application Center. Prepared under
NASA contract NSR 07-002-029. Storrs, Connecticut: NERAC, March 31, 1968.

_____. Regional Dissemination Center Impact Studies,
Nos. 1-3. Prepared under NASA contract NSR
07-002-029. Storrs, Connecticut: NERAC, 1968.

North American Aviation, Autonetics Division. Final
Report, DOD User-Needs Study: Flow of Scientific and Technical Information Within the Defense Industry. Volume I. Prepared for Office
of Director of Defense, Research and Engineering. Springfield, Virginia: Clearinghouse for
Federal Scientific and Technical Information,
November 30, 1966.

North Carolina Science and Technology Research Cen-
ter. Information from Aerospace Research to
Productive Application. Triangle Research
Park, North Carolina: NCSTRC, 1966.

Office of Industrial Application, University of
     Maryland. Continuing Studies in 1966 and 1967
     to Develop Dissemination Procedures for Use
     with the Technology Utilization Program and
     Develop In-Depth Case Histories of Commercial
     Utilization of NASA Technology Within Industry,
     Final Report. Greenbelt, Maryland: NASA,
     Goddard Space Flight Center, July 31, 1967.

RAND Corporation. Innovation and Military Require-
     ments: A Comparative Study. Prepared by
     Robert Perry for the U.S. Air Force. Santa
     Monica, California: RAND Corporation, August,
     1967.

Report of the National Conference on Technology
     Utilization and Economic Growth. Edited by
     C. Mullis. Bloomington, Indiana: ARAC, 1967.

Sherwin, Chalmers, and Raymond Isenson. "First In-
     terim Report on Project Hindsight." Report to
     the Director of Defense Research and Engineer-
     ing. Washington, D.C.: DOD, June, 1966; re-
     vised October, 1966.

Stanford Research Institute. Some Major Impacts of
     the National Space Program. Summary report
     and five detailed study volumes. Prepared for
     NASA by John Meitner, et al. Springfield, Vir-
     ginia: Clearinghouse for Federal Scientific
     and Technical Information, September, 1968.

Technology Application Center, University of New
     Mexico. Five Year Goals. Albuquerque, New
     Mexico: TAC, May 1, 1967.

Thompson Ramo Wooldridge. Technology Transfer in
     the Service of Mankind. Redondo Beach, Cali-
     fornia: TRW, 1970.

U.S. Bureau of the Budget. Standard Industrial
     Classification Manual. Washington, D.C.:
     U.S. Government Printing Office, 1967.

U.S. Department of Commerce. Review of Regional
Economic Research and Planning in New England.
Washington, D.C.: U.S. Government Printing
Office, 1966.

_____. Financing New Technological Enterprise.
Washington, D.C.: U.S. Government Printing
Office, September, 1970.

U.S. Department of Defense. Registration for Scien-
tific and Technical Information Services.
Washington, D.C.: DOD, Defense Documentation
Center, January, 1968.

U.S. Federal Council for Science and Technology.
Annual Report on Government Patent Policy.
Washington, D.C.: U.S. Government Printing
Office, June, 1966.

U.S. National Aeronautics and Space Administration.
Technology Utilization Program Review. Washington, D.C.: NASA OTU, June, 1965.

_____. Technology Utilization Program. NASA No.
N65-3650. Washington, D.C.: U.S. Government
Printing Office, 1965.

_____. How to Use NASA's Scientific and Technical
Information System. Washington, D.C.: U.S.
Government Printing Office, 1965.

_____. The Technology Utilization Program. Wash-
ington, D.C.: NASA OTU, 1965.

_____. A Survey of Space Applications. NASA SP-142.
Washington, D.C.: U.S. Government Printing
Office, April, 1967.

_____. Technology Utilization Program Review.
Washington, D.C.: NASA OTU, February, 1967.

_____. Useful New Technology from Aerospace Re-
search and Development. Washington, D.C.:
NASA OTU, 1970.

_____. Applications of Aerospace Technology in the Public Sector. Washington, D.C.: NASA OTU, 1970.

CONGRESSIONAL HEARINGS

U.S. Congress, House of Representatives, Committee on Science and Astronautics. 1968 NASA Authorization. Hearings. 90th Congress, first session. H.R. 4450 and H.R. 6470. Washington, D.C.: U.S. Government Printing Office, 1967. Parts 1 and 4.

_____. For the Benefit of All Mankind. Report. 91st Congress, second session. H.R. 91-1673. Washington, D.C.: U.S. Government Printing Office, 1970.

_____. The Management of Information and Knowledge. Report. 91st Congress, second session. Washington, D.C.: U.S. Government Printing Office, 1970. (Committee print.)

_____. Subcommittee on Advanced Research and Technology. 1967 NASA Authorization. Hearings. 89th Congress, second session. H.R. 12718. Washington, D.C.: U.S. Government Printing Office, 1966. Parts 1 and 4.

_____. 1969 NASA Authorization. Hearings. 90th Congress, second session. H.R. 15086. Washington, D.C.: U.S. Government Printing Office, 1968. Parts 1 and 4.

_____. 1970 NASA Authorization. Hearings. 91st Congress, final session. H.R. 4046, H.R. 10251. Washington, D.C.: U.S. Government Printing Office, 1969. Parts 1 and 4.

_____. 1971 NASA Authorization. Hearings. 91st Congress, second session. H.R. 15695. Washington, D.C.: U.S. Government Printing Office, 1970. Parts 1 and 4.

_____, Subcommittee on Patents and Scientific Inventions. Ownership of Inventions Developed in the Course of Federal Space Research Contracts. Report. 87th Congress, second session. Washington, D.C.: U.S. Government Printing Office, April, 1962. (Committee print.)

_____, Subcommittee on Science, Research, and Development. Technology Assessment Seminar. Report. 90th Congress, first session. Washington, D.C.: U.S. Government Printing Office, 1967.

_____, Senate, Committee on Aeronautical and Space Sciences. NASA Authorization for Fiscal Year 1968. 90th Congress, first session. S. 1296. Washington, D.C.: U.S. Government Printing Office, 1967. Parts 1 and 2.

_____. Space Program Benefits. Hearings. 91st Congress, second session. Washington, D.C.: U.S. Government Printing Office, 1970.

_____, Committee on the Judiciary, Subcommittee on Patents, Trademarks, and Copyrights. Patent Practices of the Department of Defense. Report. Washington, D.C.: U.S. Government Printing Office, September, 1961.

_____. Government Patent Policy. Hearings. 89th Congress, first session. S. 789, S. 1809, and S. 1899. Washington, D.C.: U.S. Government Printing Office, June, 1965. Parts 1 and 2.

_____, Select Committee on Small Business, Subcommittee on Science and Technology. Policy Planning for Technology Transfer. Report. Prepared by Richard Carpenter of the Science Policy Research Division of the Legislative Reference Service, Library of Congress. 90th Congress, first session. S. Doc. No. 15. Washington, D.C.: U.S. Government Printing Office, May, 1967.

_____. Technology Transfer. Hearings. 90th Congress, first session. Washington, D.C.: U.S. Government Printing Office, 1967.

_____. The Prospects for Technology Transfer. Report. 90th Congress, second session. Washington, D.C.: U.S. Government Printing Office, May, 1968.

FEDERAL STATUTES AND CASES

Atomic Energy Act of 1946. Public Law 79-585, 60 Stat., 42 U.S.C.A. 1801. (As amended 1954.)

Court of Claims. Patent Cases Act of 1948. 62 Stat., 28 U.S.C.A. 1498. (As amended 1960.)

Herbert Cooper Co. Unpublished division of the Comptroller General. B-136916. August 25, 1958.

National Aeronautics and Space Act of 1958. Public Law 85-568, 72 Stat., 42 U.S.C.A. 2451. (As amended 1964.)

INTERVIEWS

Series of interviews with Arthur D. Little, Inc., personnel, Cambridge, Massachusetts. August, 1966, to April, 1967, and November, 1968, to January, 1969.

Series of interviews with NASA Electronic Research Center TUO's, Cambridge Massachusetts. August, 1966, to March, 1967, and October, 1968, to February, 1969.

Series of interviews with NASA OTU personnel, branch chiefs, RDC administrators, and RDC operations personnel. August, 1966, to January, 1969.

Series of interviews with NASA Patent Counsel.
August, 1966, to January, 1969.

Series of interviews with NERAC industrial clients.
November, 1968, to January, 1969.

Interviews with Stanford Research Institute NASA
project personnel. November 7, 1968.

Interviews with DRI NASA project personnel. November 6, 1968, and February 20, 1969.

ADDRESSES

Carlson, Jack. "Aspects of the Diffusion of Technology in the United States." Paper presented
to the Fifth Meeting of Senior Economic Advisors, Economic Commission of Europe, United
Nations. Geneva, Switzerland, October 2, 1967.

Chasen, Lawrence. "Availability of Information and
Means of Transfer." Paper presented at the
Joint Engineering Management Conference.
Philadelphia, Pennsylvania, September 30, 1968.

Harnett, Daniel. Statement before the House Committee on Science and Astronautics. March, 1971.

Milliken, Gordon, and John Gilmore. "The Transfer-
ability of Aerospace Management Technology."
Aerospace Industries Association of America,
Space Projections from the Rocky Mountain Region. Denver, Colorado, July 15-16, 1968.

Philips, Ronald. Presentation to ICMA/NASA Working
Conference on Technology Transfer. Washington,
D.C., October 21-23, 1970.

Price, William J. "Key Role of a Mission-Oriented
Agency's Scientific Research Activities." Prepared for Symposium on Interaction of Science
and Technology. University of Illinois,
Urbana, Illinois, October 17-18, 1967.

_____. "Scientific Research and Innovation." Pre-
    pared for Symposium on the Innovative Process
    in Industry, American Chemical Society Meeting.
    San Francisco, California, April 2, 1968.

Roberts, Edward, and Herbert Wainer. "Technology
    Transfer and Entrepreneurial Success." Paper
    presented to the Twentieth National Conference
    on the Administration of Research. Miami
    Beach, Florida, October 26, 1966.

                UNPUBLISHED PAPERS AND REPORTS

Allen, Thomas J. "The Differential Performance of
    Information Channels in the Transfer of Tech-
    nology." Working paper, Alfred P. Sloan
    School of Management. Cambridge, Massachusetts:
    MIT Sloan School, June, 1966.

Allen, Thomas J., and Stephen Cohen. "Information
    Flow in an R&D Laboratory." Working paper,
    Alfred P. Sloan School of Management. Cam-
    bridge, Massachusetts: MIT Sloan School,
    August, 1966.

Allen, Thomas J., Arthur Gerstenfeld, and Peter G.
    Gerstberger. "The Problem of Internal Consult-
    ing in Research and Development Organizations."
    Working paper, Alfred P. Sloan School of Man-
    agement. Cambridge, Massachusetts: MIT Sloan
    School, July, 1968.

Grabowski, Henry G. "The Determinants and Effects
    of Industrial Research and Development." Un-
    published doctoral dissertation, Econometric
    Research Program. Princeton University, Sep-
    tember, 1966.

Hayes, Richard. "A Study of the Transfer of Technol-
    ogy from Government Sponsored R&D to Commercial
    Operations in Selected Electronic Companies."
    Unpublished doctoral dissertation. American
    University. (Available from the Technology
    Utilization Office, NASA Headquarters, Washing-
    ton, D.C.)

Kleiman, Herbert. "The Integrated Circuit: A Case Study of Product Innovation in the Electronics Industry." Unpublished doctoral dissertation. Washington, D.C.: School of Business Administration, George Washington University, June, 1966.

National Planning Association. "The Impact of the U.S. Civilian Space Program on the U.S. Domestic Economy." Report prepared for the Lockheed Aircraft Corporation. Washington, D.C.: NPA, July, 1965.

Shimshoni, Daniel. "Aspects of Scientific Entrepreneurship." Unpublished doctoral dissertation. Kennedy School of Government, Harvard University, May, 1966.

Utterback, James. "The Process of Technical Innovation in Instrument Firms." Unpublished doctoral dissertation. Cambridge, Massachusetts: MIT Sloan School, January, 1969.

Wainer, Herbert, and Irwin Rubin. "Motivation of R&D Entrepreneurs: Determinants of Company Success." Working paper, Alfred P. Sloan School of Management. Cambridge, Massachusetts: MIT Sloan School, January, 1967.

Watson, Donald, and Mary Holman. "Evaluation of NASA's Patent Policies." Washington, D.C.: George Washington University, Department of Economics, 1966.

Wolek, Francis. "User Studies and the Transfer of Innovation: Implications of Past Research." Philadelphia: Wharton School, University of Pennsylvania, 1967.

NASA Regional Dissemination
  Centers (cont'd)
  funding (table), 84
  locations and dates of es-
    tablishment (table), 54
  vs. other sources of tech-
    nology, 137-38
  recommendations, 169-70
  self-support requirement, 42,
    64-65, 81-84, 168
  surveys of effectiveness,
    13-15, 20, 22-23, 42, 106,
    165-66
  See also ARAC client survey,
    Congressional; ARAC/NERAC
    client surveys; ARAC/NERAC
    study; NASA technology
    transfer; NERAC
NASA Scientific and Technical
  Information Division, 5-6,
  71, 72-73, 75
NASA technology acquisition, 6
NASA technology evaluation, 6
NASA technology transfer
  Congressional study, 13-15
  vs. dissemination, 53, 165-67
  DRI studies. See Denver Re-
    search Institute studies
  expenditures, 5-6
  general vs. specific, 64,
    131-38, 141, 153, 165, 168
  Hayes study, 22-23, 41
  Little study, 24, 32-34, 41,
    42, 164, 167
  policies inhibiting, 8, 42,
    64-65, 136, 153-157
  policies promoting, 72
  recommendations, 169-71
  slowness, 63, 136
  and technical base of trans-
    feree, 63-64, 136-37, 143-
    51, 158
  Watson and Holman study, 29,
    35-38
  See also ARAC; ARAC client
    survey, Congressional;
    ARAC/NERAC client surveys;
    ARAC/NERAC study; NASA Re-
    gional Dissemination Cen-
    ters; NASA Technology Utili-
    zation Program; Tech Briefs

NASA Technology Utilization
  Program, 5-6, 8-9, 14, 19-20,
  32, 53, 60-63, 72-78, 171
  distribution policies, 75-79
  lag in RDC reporting, 99
  organization, 73
  publications, 74-75
  reports of contractors, 75
  services provided, 76-79
  See also NASA Regional Dis-
    semination Centers; NASA
    technology transfer
NERAC, 85-90
  fees and funds received, 86-
    87
  lack of NASA support, 89-90
  lack of university support,
    87
  marketing strategies, 89
  services and personnel, 90
  See also ARAC/NERAC client
    surveys; ARAC/NERAC study
New England Research Application Center. See NERAC

Patent Cases Act (1948), 36
Patent policy studies, 34-35,
  39-40
Patents and licenses, 7, 36
Payoff rate, space/defense vs.
  commercial R&D, 61
Pittsburgh, University of, 77
Polaroid Corporation, 98
Policy Planning for Technology
  Transfer (Carpenter), 174
Project Hindsight, 34

Raytheon Corporation, 98
RDC's. See NASA Regional Dissemination Centers
Research and development programs, federal, 3-4, 31-39,
  69-72
  and agency policies, 69-72
  payoff rate of, vs. commer-
    cial, 61
  recommendations, 169-71
  unresolved questions, 171-74
  See also NASA technology
    transfer; Technology trans-
    fer

226

ABOUT THE AUTHOR

Samuel I. Doctors, associate professor on the faculty of the Graduate School of Management, Northwestern University, has had wide experience in technology transfer in the federal agency context. He has served as a consultant to private firms engaged in transfer and to the NASA Technology Utilization Program. He has worked as an aerospace engineer for a number of firms, including Honeywell, General Motors, and Westinghouse, working on various aspects of the space program.

Professor Doctors holds a doctorate in Business Administration from the Harvard Business School and a law degree from the Harvard Law School. Before coming to Northwestern he spent a year teaching courses in operations and technological management at the Harvard Business School.

Professor Doctors has published two books and a number of articles on various aspects of technological management. Most recently he has acted as a consultant to the Office of Economic Opportunity in the area of minority economic development and to the President's Advisory Council on Minority Business Enterprise.